Haunted Teachers

TRUE GHOST STORIES

by ALLAN ZULLO

SCHOLASTIC INC.

New York Toronto London Auckland Sydney
Mexico City New Delhi Hong Kong Buenos Aires

To my good friend Nick Griffis,
who teaches literacy not from a book
but from the heart.

No part of this publication may be reproduced, stored in a retrieval system, or transmitted in any form or by any means, electronic, mechanical, photocopying, recording, or otherwise, without written permission of the publisher. For information regarding permission, write to Scholastic Inc., Attention: Permissions Department, 557 Broadway, New York, NY 10012.

ISBN 0-439-68060-3

Copyright © 1996 by The Wordsellers, Inc. All rights reserved. Published by Scholastic Inc. SCHOLASTIC and associated logos are trademarks and/or registered trademarks of Scholastic Inc.

12 11 10 9 8 7 6 6 7 8 9 10/0

Printed in the U.S.A. 40

First Scholastic Printing, January 2005

Cover illustrations by Patrick Faricy
Cover design by Jennifer Rinaldi Windau

www.allanzullo.com

CONTENTS

Does a ghost haunt your teacher?

Ghosts have haunted all sorts of people, such as doctors, lawyers, parents, kids—and even teachers! In schools new and old, teachers have reported seeing phantoms that often appeared to be the spirits of former teachers.

In some cases experts were called in to investigate these so-called hauntings. Usually, the experts walked away baffled. All they knew for sure was that something weird had happened that couldn't be fully explained.

This book is a creepy collection of stories about phantoms—especially ghostly teachers—who have haunted teachers and students in the classroom, on the playground, and at home. These eerie tales are inspired, in part, by real-life cases taken from the files of noted ghost hunters. The names and places in the stories are not real.

Does the spirit of a teacher haunt your classroom? Is your teacher spooked by a ghost? You might think so after reading the startling stories in this book!

The Phantom Rider

I*s that a horse I hear galloping?* Connie Hall looked up from her desk and walked toward the window of her second-floor classroom. The teacher, who had stayed late after school to mark papers, peered out into the darkness but failed to see anything unusual.

The sound of horse hoofs rumbling across the school property grew louder. She opened the window and stuck her head out. *Judging from the noise, the horse should be right outside, but I don't see it,* thought Connie. *What would a horse be doing around here? This is a well-developed suburb. There certainly aren't any horses nearby.*

Connie was about to return to her desk when she heard a faint voice utter in despair, "Where is my school? Where are my children?"

The teacher poked her head out the window again and yelled, "Hello, who's out there?"

For a brief moment in the moonless night, she spotted

something moving away, beyond the range of the blue security light that shined on the playground below. *I wonder what that was,* Connie thought. *Maybe someone was riding a horse after all. Oh, well, I better get back to grading my papers.*

It wasn't unusual for the seventh-grade teacher to work alone at night in her classroom at Fletcher Middle School in the town of Mercer. Single with no kids, the slightly overweight 42-year-old woman had devoted her life to her profession since her divorce ten years ago. She put in more hours than any other teacher in the school. And it paid off. Her students always scored higher than the county average on aptitude tests because Connie had a knack for inspiring them. She projected a warmth about her that made kids instantly like her. She flashed a ready smile and made each student feel special. Kids called her "Hugger" Hall because of her penchant for hugging her students. "You're never too old to hug or get hugged," she'd say.

Often Connie would stay after class and then join friends for dinner at a nearby barbecue restaurant. She would return to the school and take care of all the things that teachers must do when they aren't actually teaching. Around 9 P.M., she would go to the fitness center for a workout that never seemed to shed any pounds.

Connie had forgotten about the horse incident until one evening several weeks later when she was decorating her classroom for Halloween. Once again she heard a horse galloping by the school. This time it sounded as if the horse had slowed to a canter near the playground. Connie saw nothing out the window. But she wasn't satisfied, so she walked down the stairs and went outside, locking the door behind her.

I definitely heard a horse snorting, she told herself. *I'm not imagining this.* As she turned the corner of the building, she expected to see the horse, but the playground was empty. Connie stood still for a minute listening to the sounds of the night. Cars rumbled past the front of the school, and a siren screeched in the distance. Nothing unusual.

Connie unlocked the door and walked back into the school. As she started for the stairs, she caught a glimpse of a figure in gray clothes striding down the hall.

"Hello," said Connie. "Who's there?"

The person kept walking away from her, stopping at every classroom door as if looking for someone or something.

"Yoo-hoo! Hello?" Connie shouted. Still no response.

In the darkened hallway Connie could barely make out that the person was a woman with wavy blond hair, wearing a wide-brimmed hat and a long cape. When the woman reached the end of the corridor, she simply vanished.

Connie stood stunned for a long minute before running to the end of the hallway. *How could she disappear like that?* the awed teacher asked herself. *That's impossible!* Connie checked the last two classroom doors on either side of the corridor, but they were both locked. *Who was she? Where did she go? How did she get in here—and more importantly, how did she get out?*

Connie felt a chill squirm across her back. She pulled her button-down sweater tightly around her neck and headed for the stairs. Then she heard the horse gallop off. Connie quickly rushed to the back entrance, flung open the door, and caught a brief glimpse of a figure in gray, riding on a horse into the darkness.

The next day Connie questioned all the teachers and staff and learned that no one had been in school the night before. After she told the janitor, Mr. Blythe, what had happened, he chuckled and said, "Sounds like you have a ghost on your hands."

"What makes you say that?" asked Connie.

"A few years ago another teacher, whose name I can't remember, said she saw a woman in gray on a horse galloping outside the school one night. The maintenance man back then, George Raines, said it was probably the Phantom Rider. Well, I never heard tell of such a thing. It seems that once in a great while, a ghostly woman and her horse like to ride past our school. I don't pay much attention to this stuff, but maybe you were given the privilege of seeing the Phantom Rider herself."

"That's a little hard to swallow," said Connie. "I never heard about this legend before. But maybe I'll do a little research—just for fun, of course."

At the library she found a book on local legends that mentioned the Phantom Rider this way:

"She often rides through the night on a palomino stallion in north Mercer. She wears a gray cloak that floats behind her, and her blond hair streams in the wind. Both hands grasp the reins as she comes out of the past, is visible only briefly, and vanishes into the darkness as if all the legions of another world are in pursuit."

When Connie read the description of the phantom, her heart began to race and her mouth grew dry. *That describes exactly the person I saw in the hallway! Could the Phantom Rider be real?*

Connie eagerly searched the shelves but found no other books containing information about the legend. She yearned to see the phantom again, and wondered if she ever would. Connie didn't have to wait long.

Working late one night alone in the classroom, Connie was reading papers from her students about the effects the Civil War had on the area. She was extremely pleased with the quality of the reports—including one about a young banker named Charles Waldrop who headed a local Confederate militia. One day he encountered a squad of Union soldiers and, while on his trusty steed, let them pursue him through the woods and past the schoolhouse. As the Yankees rode by the school, members of the rebel militia stuck their guns out of the school windows and fired away, killing all six enemy soldiers. Waldrop had lured them past the school on purpose and led them straight into a Confederate ambush.

While she read, Connie became aware of a distant sound. *The galloping horse! I hear it whinnying. The phantom must be back!* The tiny hairs on the back of the teacher's neck stood up. Connie was on her way to the window when her body jerked from surprise.

Standing in the doorway was a woman whose wavy blond hair flowed from under a battered Confederate hat. A long gray cape hid most of an ankle-length dress and her black high-top button-down shoes.

"You startled me," said Connie. "Who are you and how did you get in here?"

The woman, in her early 20s, didn't speak. Connie noticed the woman's face looked extremely pale, her drawn eyes hollow and sunken cheeks tear-stained. Her thin lips had fallen in an expression of sorrow and bewilderment. *With makeup, different clothes, and a smile, she could look really pretty*, thought Connie. *She's obviously troubled.*

"Where are my children?" the woman whimpered.

"Perhaps if you tell me who you are and the names of your children, I might be able to help you."

"My students. I'm looking for my students."

"Are you a teacher?"

The woman nodded.

"Where?"

"Here."

"You must be mistaken," said Connie. "I teach here at Fletcher, and I know everyone on the faculty. Who are you?"

"Sally Foster," replied the woman. "Help me find my students," she said pleadingly. Sally stepped back into the hallway out of Connie's sight.

"Wait, don't go." Connie scurried out into the hallway. Sally was gone. Connie ran down the stairs and stood in the front of the lobby, expecting to hear footsteps or a door close. But all was quiet until she heard the galloping of a horse heading off into the night.

What just happened here? Connie asked herself. *Could she be the strange woman I saw in the hallway? Long cloak, hat, blond hair. Why, she could be the Phantom Rider! How exciting! But if so, why is she haunting this school? And who are the children she asks about? I must find the answers, or I'll never be able to rest.*

Connie was too pumped to read any more papers. Her whole body shook from excitement over seeing what she now believed was a ghost. She gathered her things and drove to the fitness center, hoping the workout would calm her down.

That Saturday Connie went to the county historical society. She scoured dusty old books and yellowed papers from the Civil War days.

She discovered that the school where the rebel troops had hidden and ambushed the Yankees was situated on Miller Road, a mile (1.6 km) north of the city dam—the exact location where Fletcher Middle School now stood. What she learned next really jolted her: The last person to teach at the school was named Sally Foster.

There's no denying it, thought Connie. *I saw the ghost of Sally Foster! Oh, I hope I meet her again, to find out why she's haunting our school. She's so anguished. Maybe if I spoke with her, I could help ease her torment. And I do so want to know why she's looking for her students.*

Night after night Connie waited in her classroom, hoping to encounter the spirit from the past. A week went by without any sign of Sally or her horse. One evening, in frustration, Connie drew Sally's name in big bold letters on the blackboard and shouted, "Sally Foster, where are you?"

"Help me, please."

Connie whirled around and saw Sally standing in the middle of the room. "Sally, you've come back. How can I help you?"

"My school, my students. Where are they?"

"Sally, they're not here. That was a long time ago. What happened to you? Why are you dressed like a rebel soldier?"

Sally clutched at her cloak as if it offered protection against the heartache of the past. Slowly she began to walk around the room, gingerly touching the students' desks and lightly fingering the cabinets and countertops.

"I loved teaching," said Sally. "That's all I wanted to do with my life. Teach, get married, and have children. That's not asking so much."

She smiled for the first time. "I taught in the most beautiful little schoolhouse you can imagine. Whitewashed every summer. I taught 14 children, all wonderfully sweet and delightfully energetic. I loved them all. Do you know where they are? I've been looking for them."

"No, Sally, I don't." Connie was afraid to tell Sally that they had died long ago; that more than 130 years had passed.

"I don't suppose you do," Sally murmured. She strolled toward the front of the room. "Where is the wishing well?"

"We don't have a wishing well."

Sally shook her head. "Everything has changed, yet nothing has changed."

"What about the well, Sally?"

"In the schoolyard was a wishing well. That's where I met my sweetheart, Charles Waldrop."

"The banker who headed the local Confederate militia?"

"Why, yes, do you know him?"

"I know of him."

Sally twirled around once and threw her head back. "Charles was so handsome. He and I would spend hours by the wishing well. It was said that if you wished hard enough before you drank from the well, your wish would come true. We wished to be married and spend the rest of our lives together. But then the war between the states broke out and ruined everything.

"One day, the Yankees were advancing on the town. Charles came to the schoolhouse and told me to take the children and run for the hills, that it wasn't safe to stay in the school."

"I read about how the rebels ambushed the Yankees at the school," said Connie.

Sally nodded. "The children and I were running deep into the woods when we encountered a platoon of Yankees. The children panicked and ran in all directions. I tried to keep them together but it was no use. I grabbed four little ones and took them with me. The Yankees found us and held us briefly before they let us go on our way.

"Eventually, I returned the four little ones to their homes. But I had to find the other children. I ran back toward the school. I had reached the wishing well when I noticed that the Yankees now occupied the schoolhouse, not the rebels. And then I saw . . ." Sally began to cry.

"Sally, what's wrong?"

"It's so hard to talk about it." Her arms were folded tightly across her chest, and her head hung low as she continued. "I saw Charles's dead body. After the ambush, Charles was caught by the Yankees. Rather than surrender, he tried to shoot his way to freedom. But the Yankees shot him to death. The soldiers draped his body over his horse, a beautiful palomino named Charger, and brought him back to the schoolyard.

"It took all that was within me to keep from crying out in grief. But I held my tongue and remained crouched behind the well. Charles's horse was tied up not more than ten yards (9.1 m) away from where I hid. I waited for my chance and sneaked up to Charger and whispered for him to stay calm, which he did. And then, in a flash, I untied him, hopped on, and rode off with Charles's body right out from under the noses of those bluecoats!"

A smug grin spread across her pale face. An instant later, her expression changed to sorrow. "I was riding off not knowing at first where I was going. I simply wanted to be with my beloved. I soon arrived at his parents' house. And there we all sat and wept.

"Later that night I had to make sure the rest of the children—my students—had safely returned to their houses. I donned Charles's hat and cape—to feel close to him—and rode Charger into the woods where I last saw the children fleeing. I don't remember much after that. Shots rang out. I felt a sharp pain here." Sally untied the cape and pointed to a spot below her neck.

Connie gasped at the sight of a dark red bloodstain on Sally's blouse running from her collar down to her waist.

"You were shot!" cried Connie.

"Evidently. Charger was felled too. I don't know what happened after that or where I went, because it was so dark, so very dark. I kept looking for my children, those sweet young things who were put in my care. I kept searching and searching and couldn't find them. And then I went back to the schoolhouse—only it wasn't there. I have lost my beloved, my school, and my students. Do you know where my children are? Help me find my students, my school. Help me." And then Sally slowly faded away.

"Come back, Sally. Come back." Then Connie heard the galloping horse. She knew that Sally's ghost had left.

The teacher's knees began to wobble, and she slipped into a student's desk to steady herself. The last few minutes had been the most extraordinary of her life. *I was talking face-to-face with a ghost! She was right here in my classroom. A teacher who lived in the last century, who has never been able to rest in peace, spoke to me! I have to know more about her.*

Connie returned to the county historical society and searched for more information on Sally Foster and Charles Waldrop. She didn't find anything and was about to give up. As she reached for a directory, she accidentally knocked a shoe box off the shelf. When it hit the floor, several letters fell out. She put them back in the box and was placing it on the shelf when she noticed that an old letter, folded in fourths, had slipped under a table.

She picked it up. Curious, Connie opened it. Dated January 5, 1918, it was from Douglas Waldrop. *Waldrop?* thought Connie. *Could he be related to Charles?* The letter was addressed to Miss Hannah Tripp of Mercer, who Connie later learned was a local author. Hannah had been gathering material for a book on local legends when she unexpectedly died in 1920. The shoe box contained Hannah's notes and research material. *I absolutely have to read this letter,* Connie said to herself.

* * *

My Dear Miss Tripp,

You asked if I had any knowledge of a supposed Phantom Rider who gallops on a magnificent palomino near Miller Road. The answer is yes. I have firsthand knowledge which you are free to use any way you wish.

I am near 70 years old now, but what I am about to tell you is as clear to me as when it happened back in 1861 when I was 11 years old.

My older brother Charles fought for the Confederacy and led the Yankees into a deadly ambush at the schoolhouse in Mercer. Unfortunately, he was killed hours later. Meanwhile, his fiancée, the schoolteacher Sally Foster, was leading her students to safety when they encountered a battle. Panic broke out and the children scattered in all directions. She tried to round them up but couldn't.

Sally, a marvelous woman with smarts to match her bravery and beauty, managed to retrieve Charles's body and his palomino Charger from the grasp of the Yankees and return to our home. There, we mourned our loss.

Later that same day, in Charles's hat and cloak, Sally rode on Charger to find her missing students. Tragically, she and Charger were slain by enemy bullets. Her fatal ride was unnecessary, for all the children had arrived home safely.

The Yankees were so angered by the ambush that they burned the schoolhouse to the ground. They left nothing. They even carted off the stone from the school's foundation to help build a wall from which to fire upon the Confederates.

Two days later Charles and Sally were buried side by

side. The night after their funeral I was walking home from the cemetery. In the distance came pounding hoof beats. On and on they came, past the church, past the graveyard, and on toward the schoolyard.

In the moonlight I saw something I could not believe. For it was Charger, and upon him was none other than Sally Foster herself, wearing my brother's Confederate cavalry cape and hat.

I had never seen such an awesome sight. The hoofs scarcely seemed to touch the ground. Charger came to a stop directly in front of me. While the horse stood motionless, the wind and dust swirled up in a cloud, and I heard Sally Foster ask, "Where are my children? Where is my school?" Charger reared up, and then they sped off into the night.

I thought my grief from the death of my brother and his fiancée (of whom I was most fond) had caused me to see things. Surely, what I saw could not have been real, I told myself. But an astounding incident that happened the following month convinced me otherwise.

One night I had sneaked up upon a Union campsite next to where the school once stood. Suddenly there was a hue and cry. The sentries yelled that a Confederate soldier was fast approaching from the east on a horse. The sentries ordered the horseman to stop, and when their call was not obeyed, they raised their rifles and fired. A salvo of bullets flew from a dozen guns. Yet the horse and rider did not fall, but continued to advance. To the soldiers' astonishment, they saw that the rider was a woman. I was even more amazed, for the horse was Charger and the rider was Sally

Foster! As she reached the perimeter of the camp, she shouted, "Where are my children? Where is my school?" Charger reared up and then galloped right through the camp before being swallowed by the darkness. The men stood in silence, unable to fathom what they had witnessed. Even I, who had observed the specter weeks earlier, found it hard to believe.

I have not seen Charger and Sally—whom people now call the Phantom Rider—since. But over the years I have heard of others who claim to have seen her. It's always by the spot where the school once stood. Sadly, I suspect she is doomed to roam the area forever, looking for her students and her school.

So, if anyone should ask you if the Phantom Rider is a legend, tell him no, it is not a legend. Tell him it is absolutely true.

Very Truly Yours,
Douglas Waldrop

Connie's hand trembled when she put down the letter. Now it became crystal clear to her why Sally Foster had made those ghostly appearances at Fletcher Middle School. It was also apparent what Connie must say the next time she saw Sally.

About a week later, alone in her classroom, Connie heard the galloping horse. Within a minute Sally Foster appeared in the back of the room.

"I'm so tired, so weary," Sally moaned. "Do you know where my children are? Do you know what happened to my school?"

"Yes, I know the answers, Sally. Your students all made it safely home. No harm came to them. They grew up and are gone now."

"And my school? Why can't I find my school?"

"I'm sorry to tell you this, Sally, but it was destroyed. The soldiers burned it down."

Sally began to weep. "My whole life was tied up in that school—the children, the wishing well, my fiancé. All gone, all gone. Now what shall I do?"

"Sally, it's time for you to move on. You don't need to haunt this place anymore. It's a different school, with new students and teachers who love them very much. There's nothing more for you and Charger to do here. Your search is finally over."

Sally didn't say a word. She seemed deep in thought. Finally, she said, "Yes, perhaps you're right. Charger and I can rest now." The anguish that had been etched in her face was replaced by a peaceful glow. "We can rest," she repeated as she faded away.

Connie ran to the window and looked down onto the playground. The security light shined on Sally Foster, who sat tall and straight atop her sturdy palomino. The horse reared up, pawing at the air with its front legs as if in happiness and relief. Then he and his mistress galloped off into the night never to be seen again.

Curse of the Egyptian Bone

Middle-school teacher Carter Sexton was grading papers at his desk early one morning when student Kyle Phillips entered the otherwise empty classroom. Kyle was holding a paper bag.

Carter looked up from his desk. "Morning, Kyle. I'm sorry to hear of your grandfather's death. Are you okay?"

"Yes, Mr. Sexton, thank you. I'm fine."

"What's in the bag?"

"My grandmother gave this to me yesterday. It belonged to Grandpa Stan, and now that he's gone, she wanted me to have it. I thought that because we were studying about bones and stuff, I'd share it with the class." He gently pulled out a glass case shaped like a bell that fit over a wooden base. Inside the case was an oddly shaped bone.

Suddenly, sweat burst from Carter's forehead. His heart began beating like a jackhammer. *No, it can't be!* he told himself. *It's not possible. That was destroyed years ago.*

This must be different. It can't be the same one.

"Mr. Sexton, is something the matter?"

"I'm fine, Kyle," the teacher replied in a shaky voice. "May I?"

Kyle placed the case in Carter's shaking hands. The teacher was so nervous he had to set the case down on his desk. He lifted the glass cover and picked up the bone. A wave of nausea swept over him. He put it down and gulped. Then he looked at the faded, partially torn label on the base. "Sacrum from an Egyptian princess, found in 1951 by Zel—" The rest of the label was missing.

Carter buried his face in his hands and muttered to himself. "I don't understand. How is it possible?"

"Mr. Sexton? You're acting a little weird."

A look of terror flared up in the teacher's eyes. He clutched Kyle's arm and said, "We must destroy this bone at once!"

"What are you talking about?" snapped Kyle as he quickly scooped up the bone and put it back in the glass case. "It's mine. It's been in my family for years."

"No, Kyle, it's not yours. This bone belongs to an ancient Egyptian princess—one whose ghost is bent on revenge. The bone is cursed. We must destroy it before it destroys us and, possibly, this school!"

Carter asked Kyle to sit down and listen to the incredible story of the curse of the Egyptian bone.

In 1951, when Carter was six years old, his parents, Alex and Zelda Sexton, left him in the care of relatives and went on a vacation to Egypt. Zelda taught science at Wilson High;

Alex taught geography at Jefferson Junior High. Every year during spring break, they traveled to an exotic locale.

In Egypt they visited the tomb of the boy king Tutankhamen, the Temple at Luxor, the Sphinx, and other famous ancient sites. They also rode in the desert of the Valley of the Kings on the backs of camels.

Knowing of their adventurous spirit, their local guide, Anwar, took them to unusual places that most tourists never got the chance to see. "How would you like to visit a tomb that even the archaeologists don't know about yet?" Anwar asked them.

"We'd love it!" Zelda declared.

"It was discovered by tomb robbers," Anwar said. "Unfortunately, they stole everything of value inside, but there is still much to see."

"Oh, this is so exciting!" said Zelda.

Anwar lit a torch and led the Sextons to the tomb's entrance and down dozens of tiny steps carved out of solid rock. The corridor was so narrow and tight that Alex's broad shoulders touched both sides of the walls. When they reached the main chamber, the Sextons both gasped. There, on a stone slab, lay a skeleton amid scraps and twists of winding cloth.

"I believe this skeleton was once a princess," said Anwar. "See the drawings on the wall. As you know, the ancient Egyptians tried to preserve bodies of those from the upper classes into mummies. They believed that the dead lived on in the next world, and that the body had to be preserved forever so it could serve that person."

"It doesn't look like their embalming method worked too

well on this body," said Zelda, scribbling in her notebook. "It's just a skeleton."

"You must remember that this skeleton is over 3,000 years old. The tomb robbers unwrapped the mummy looking for gold and jewelry inside. When the body was exposed to the air, it decayed, leaving only the bones."

After about ten minutes of examining the tomb, Anwar suggested they leave. Reluctantly, the couple followed Anwar up the narrow steps and out of the tomb into the sunlight.

"That was fantastic, Anwar," said Alex. "This definitely was the highlight of our trip. I can't wait to tell our students back home about it."

"Would you excuse me for a moment?" Zelda said. "I want to go down there again for just a second to take a few more notes. I'll be right back." She ducked into the tomb and returned a minute later.

At the hotel in Cairo later that evening, the Sextons were getting ready for dinner when Zelda walked over to Alex and smiled. Both her hands were behind her back.

"I know that look on your face, Zelda. What's up?"

"I have a confession to make," she revealed. "I took a little souvenir from the tomb." She held out her right hand. In her palm lay a strange-looking bone. "It belonged to the skeleton of the princess." It was the sacrum—the triangular-shaped bone from the lower part of the spinal column that is attached to the pelvis.

"Zelda!" exclaimed Alex. "How could you?"

"I couldn't help it. It was a once-in-a-lifetime opportunity, and I wanted a souvenir. I couldn't resist. It was like the skeleton was begging me to take it. Don't be angry with me."

"I'm not, darling." Alex picked up the bone and examined it in his hand. He smiled and said, "This will make an excellent conversation piece."

"And think of our students. What a fascinating learning tool this will be when discussing ancient Egypt and its pyramids, tombs, and mummies."

"Won't Carter be surprised. He can take it to school for Show and Tell."

"Oh, I do miss our son. Someday he'll understand its significance."

When the Sextons returned home, they showed the bone from the princess's skeleton to Carter. But because he was only six years old, he didn't fully grasp its importance.

The Sextons invited several friends over to their house to tell them about their trip to Egypt. The couple showed them photos of the Great Pyramid and the Sphinx and other Egyptian ruins.

"And now for our prized possession from the trip," announced Zelda. "Ta-da!" She lifted up a bell-shaped glass case and removed the bone, which was resting on a wooden base. Then she excitedly explained how she had obtained it. One by one, the guests examined the sacrum, oohing and aahing at holding a 3,000-year-old bone.

After the artifact was passed around, Alex gingerly placed the bone in the glass case and put the case on a small table in the dining room. The Sextons and their guests soon turned to other topics as they sipped coffee in the living room.

About an hour later, they heard a crash in the dining room. Zelda dashed into the room and cried out, "Oh, no! Not the Venetian vase!" Pottery shards from an expensive antique vase that once stood on the floor lay scattered under the dining room table. "You'd think a firecracker went off inside the vase the way the pieces are strewn," she said.

As she picked up the pieces under the table, she was startled to see the bare feet of her son across the floor. "Carter?" She stood up and stared at the little boy, whose eyes were nearly shut. "Are you sleepwalking again?"

"No," he mumbled, shaking his head.

"Did you break this vase?"

"No, Mama."

"Then how did it break?"

He shrugged.

"You had nothing to do with it? It just broke on its own?"

Carter opened his eyes and extended his arms, looking for a hug from his mother. "I didn't do it, Mama. I was walking in the room, and then the thing went boom. I didn't touch it."

Zelda hugged her son. "Sweetheart, I believe you."

"I wonder what caused this," said Alex as he studied the scene. "Even if Carter was sleepwalking and accidentally hit it, the pieces of pottery wouldn't have scattered this far."

"Carter, what are you doing up?" Zelda asked her son.

"I couldn't sleep because of the lady," he replied.

"What lady?"

"I don't know. She had a funny hat, sparkly things around her neck and arms, and blue pajamas."

Zelda looked at Alex. "Do you know what he's talking about?"

Alex shook his head. "He's obviously been dreaming." He took Carter from Zelda's arms and said, "Come on, Sport, let's put you back to bed. You were dreaming."

The next morning Alex and Zelda flipped a coin to see who would be first to take the bone to school. Alex won, so he brought it to Jefferson Junior High to show off to his students. They gazed at the sacrum as he explained how the ancient Egyptians embalmed the body and turned it into a mummy by wrapping it in oils and special linen.

Later that afternoon Alex placed the bone in his desk drawer. He had promised to let another teacher borrow it for classes the next day. As Alex left the classroom, he closed the door and locked it, shaking the door handle to make sure it was secure.

When he returned the next morning, he took one look and became furious. "What is this, a joke?" he muttered under his breath. "If it is, I don't find it funny."

The students' desks had been stacked in such a manner that they formed a pyramid all the way to the ceiling. His desk was lying upside down in front of the pyramid.

"The sacrum!" Alex rushed to his desk, opened the drawer, and pulled out the glass-encased bone. "Thank heavens, it's not broken."

Principal Joseph Trillen joined Alex in examining the room for clues to the culprits. "I fear that students somehow have made a copy of the master key to the classrooms and can get in here at will," said Alex. "The windows were locked from the inside and there's no forced entry, so they couldn't have come in any other way."

"Why did they stack the desks in a pyramid?" asked Mr. Trillen.

"It could be because I talked about Egyptian mummies yesterday," said Alex.

Pointing to the upper portion of the blackboard, the principal asked, "What about these hieroglyphics?"

In large, neat print, someone had written Egyptian symbols across the blackboard. "I didn't notice the hieroglyphics before," said the teacher, surprised at the writing. "I can't be sure, but when I came into class this morning, I don't think they were there."

"What are you saying? That someone came in after you did this morning and wrote them?"

Alex shook his head. "Of course not. I'm surprised I didn't notice them before, that's all. I guess it's because I was so shocked at seeing the pyramid of desks. Still, it's awfully hard to believe I didn't notice them."

"What do the hieroglyphics mean, Alex?"

"I don't know. At first glance they appear genuine. Whoever went to all this trouble at least learned something about ancient Egypt."

Alex copied the symbols on a piece of paper to show Zelda later. After enlisting the aid of bewildered students, who helped dismantle the pyramid and put the desks back into rows, Alex handed the sacrum over to geography teacher Betty McDonald. At the end of the day, she returned the bone to him.

"How did your students like the sacrum?" asked Alex.

"Oh, they enjoyed it," Betty answered. "But the strangest thing happened. At every one of my classes, I pulled down the roll-up map to point out where Egypt was. And then the moment I started talking about the sacrum, the map snapped up on its own. That never happened before."

"This seems to be a day of strange things," he said.

Alex brought the Egyptian bone home with him that night and told Zelda about the incidents at school.

"Obviously, what happened in your classroom was a nasty prank," said Zelda. "What happened in Betty's classroom was probably a coincidence."

Alex showed her the hieroglyphics he had copied off the blackboard. "I'll see if I can find someone at the college who can read them," she said. She took the glass-encased sacrum and set it on the kitchen counter.

Late that night, Carter ran into his parents' room and jumped on their bed. "Mommy, Daddy, I saw the lady again."

"Who, Carter?" asked Zelda.

"The lady from the other night," the little boy replied. "The one with the funny hat and sparkly things."

"Did she do or say anything to you?"

"No, she was in her blue pajamas and floated over my bed and looked down at me. How can she float in the air like that, Mommy?"

"Carter, it's just a dream," said Zelda. "Would you like to spend the night with us?"

The little boy nodded and snuggled between his parents. He was about to doze off when they all heard a thud.

"What was that?" Zelda asked fearfully.

"It came from the kitchen," Alex said. He threw on his robe and ran down the stairs. The sacrum's glass case had fallen off the kitchen counter and onto the ceramic tile floor. The bone had rolled out and was resting against a chair several feet away. The impact should have shattered the glass case, but, remarkably, the glass and the bone were not broken.

When he returned to the bedroom, Alex told Zelda, "I'm baffled. There is no earthly reason why the glass case fell off the counter by itself and that it didn't break."

The next day Zelda took the sacrum to her school to show her students. She described in detail the tomb it came from. She told them everything except how she had taken it from the skeleton of the ancient Egyptian princess.

After the final class of the day, Zelda placed the glass-encased bone on top of her desk. She left the room, locking the door behind her. When she returned the next morning, she opened the classroom door and let out a scream of anguish.

"Look at this room!" Zelda cried out to the other teachers who had rushed to her side when they heard her shriek. "It looks like someone came in here with a bulldozer! This is terrible!"

Teachers gasped with astonishment when they peered inside. Every desk—all thirty of them as well as Zelda's—had been smashed to smithereens. Posters and maps had been ripped off the walls.

"Oh, my! The sacrum!" Zelda dove into the mess, shoving aside splinters, books, and papers. Minutes later, she shouted, "Eureka! This is amazing!" Amid the rubble, she held up the glass case. Incredibly, it was not damaged. Neither was the Egyptian bone. "Look, everyone. The only thing not damaged in this whole room is the sacrum!"

Suddenly, her eyes caught a series of Egyptian hieroglyphics on the blackboard. She got to her feet and walked over to it. "I didn't write this."

She reached into her purse and pulled out the copy of

hieroglyphics that had been written on the blackboard in her husband's classroom. They were identical to the ones on her blackboard.

The police were called to investigate the vandalism—the worst in the history of Wilson High. They believed that the vandalism at Wilson and the prank at Jefferson were definitely connected.

Meanwhile, Zelda called a friend of hers, Dr. Miller Gaston, a professor of archaeology at a nearby college, who had worked on several sites in Egypt. He hurried to Zelda's classroom and examined the hieroglyphics on the blackboard. After comparing them with those in a little book of his, he let out a low whistle.

"Zelda, this might be more serious than you think."

"What do you mean, Miller?"

"The hieroglyphics say, 'Be warned. You will be cast into the darkness for eternity.' Zelda, this appears to be a death threat!"

That night at home, Alex paced back and forth, staring at the glass-encased bone. "Look at the facts, Zelda," he said. "Our vase in the dining room mysteriously explodes. Desks are formed into a pyramid in my classroom. I receive a hieroglyphic death threat on the blackboard. The sacrum's display case unexplainably falls off the kitchen counter—and doesn't break. Then everything in your classroom is smashed—except for the sacrum and its glass case. And you receive the same death threat."

"What are you saying, Alex?"

"I'm saying that the bone is cursed."

"That's ridiculous!"

"Is it? It makes sense to me. We're being punished because you stole the sacrum from the skeleton."

"The curse of the mummy?" she asked with a sarcastic laugh. "Give me a break, Alex. Have you been reading comic books instead of *National Geographic*?"

"How else do you explain everything that's happened to us since we brought back the sacrum?"

"As a science teacher, I believe there's an explanation for everything. Our classrooms were obviously targets of vandals, that's all."

"Vandals who can break into classrooms without any forced entry?" Alex scoffed. "Vandals who know ancient Egyptian hieroglyphics? I tell you, this bone is haunted or cursed—or both!"

"Mommy, Daddy, are you fighting?" called Carter, who was sitting on a step near the top of the stairs.

"Oh, sweetheart, I'm so sorry if Mommy and Daddy were talking too loudly," said Zelda as she raced up the steps and hugged her son. "We were just having a discussion. We didn't mean to wake you."

"Oh, you didn't. The lady did."

"The one you've seen before in your dreams?"

"Uh-huh," he replied. "She was floating over my bed, and this time she was laughing."

Alex took Carter from his mother and said, "Carter, I want to show you some pretty pictures in a book, okay?"

Zelda whispered to her husband, "Alex, what are you doing?"

"I have a hunch about this lady," he replied as he carried Carter downstairs into the den. Alex pulled out a book about

Egypt and, with Carter on his lap, began flipping through it. "Aren't these pretty pictures, Carter?"

The little boy nodded. After more pages and pictures, Carter let out a squeal. "Hi, lady!"

"Carter, do you know her?" asked Alex as they stared at the color drawing. It showed a typical Egyptian princess wearing a rounded headdress, a gold necklace and matching bracelets, and a flowing blue dress.

"Yes, Daddy. She's the lady who floats in my room."

"Are you sure, honey?" asked Zelda.

Carter nodded. "See the funny hat and the sparkly things and her blue pajamas? That's what the lady wears."

Alex turned to Zelda and through clenched teeth hissed, "We have to get rid of the sacrum."

"No," she snapped back. "I will not."

"What more proof do you need that this bone is cursed?"

"There is no such thing as a curse, Alex!"

"Zelda, you must send the bone to Anwar in Egypt and have him put it back with the rest of the skeleton."

"I will do no such thing!"

"Then get it out of this house!"

"Your imagination is running wild."

"How's this for imagination?" Alex stormed over to the case, took out the bone, opened the front door, and hurled the sacrum against a stone wall. The bone shattered into five pieces.

"Alex! How could you!" Zelda ran outside and scooped up the pieces. She gently placed them back in the glass case. Then she put the case in the trunk of her car.

The next day, she took the broken bone to school. After

seeing that new desks had been delivered to her classroom, she visited the art department and asked teacher Jim Williams if he could repair the sacrum. "No problem," he assured her. "I have the perfect kind of glue that will hold these pieces together. The bone should be ready by the end of the day."

When the final class was over, Zelda walked into Williams's art room. He was gone, but the fixed sacrum was sitting inside the glass case. When an art student entered the room, Zelda asked, "Do you know where Mr. Williams is?"

"Oh, Mrs. Sexton, didn't you hear?" said the student. "Mr. Williams was rushed to the hospital a couple of hours ago. He was found on the floor, unconscious."

Zelda hurriedly returned to her room, put the sacrum on her desk, and then drove to the hospital. By the time she arrived, Jim had been admitted for a head injury. She went to his room and saw that his head had been bandaged. "Jim, what happened?"

"The craziest thing," he replied. "I had just finished gluing the bones back together when—now, this is going to sound ridiculous—I saw, or rather I imagined I saw, a young woman dressed in ancient Egyptian clothing floating above me. I was so startled by this vision that I leaned back in my chair. It tipped over, and I hit the back of my head on the counter behind me. I was knocked out. A student found me and by the time I came to, I was in the emergency room getting 12 stitches in my head. They're keeping me overnight to make sure I haven't suffered a concussion."

"Oh, you poor dear." Zelda reached over and held the teacher's hand. "Did you say you saw an Egyptian?"

"Yes. While I was mending your Egyptian bone I was imagining what the princess looked like. All of a sudden, this image appeared. It was like nothing I had ever seen before. I mean, it was so real. Not transparent or smoky. Now isn't that just the craziest thing you ever heard?"

"No, Jim, it isn't. I'm so sorry."

"Why? It's not your fault."

Oh, yes it is, she said to herself. *Alex was right. I need to get rid of the sacrum once and for all.*

Zelda headed back toward school. Twice on the return trip, she had to pull off to the side as fire trucks sped by. *My, there must be a big fire,* she thought. As she neared the school, she saw billowing clouds of white and gray smoke rising above the trees. *Oh, it couldn't be. Not the school. Oh, not the school!*

When Zelda turned the last corner she was stopped by a police officer. "Officer, what's going on?" she asked.

"Wilson High is on fire," he said. "You need to clear the lane for the fire trucks. It looks like a bad one."

"But I'm a teacher at Wilson!"

"Look, ma'am, there's nothing you can do."

Fighting back tears, Zelda parked the car and ran up to a crowd of spectators who were watching the flames lick out of a second-story window. In horror, the teacher realized that the fire was blazing in her classroom. *That bone!* she told herself. *That haunted bone! It's to blame for all this! I never should have taken it!*

"Zelda!" shouted English teacher Harriet Lane. "Isn't this just tragic?"

"How did it happen, Harriet?"

"No one knows. The fire started on the second floor. Thank goodness it happened at the end of the day after the students had left. I don't think anybody got hurt. What do you suppose caused it?"

"A vengeful ghost," muttered Zelda.

"A what?"

"Nothing, Harriet, nothing."

The fire, smoke, and water caused thousands of dollars of damage to classrooms on the first and second floors. That meant the school would be closed for several weeks until the completion of repairs.

The next day Zelda returned to the school and met with fire investigators who were sifting through the charred rubble looking for the cause of the blaze.

"All we know for sure is that the fire definitely started in your classroom, Mrs. Sexton," said Captain Mark Plano.

"I was in there for just a second at about 4 P.M.," she said. "Everything was fine then. When I left, I locked the door behind me."

"It was a tremendously hot fire. I'm sorry that everything in the room was destroyed."

"Hey, everybody," yelled fireman Stan Phillips, who had been poking around the burnt remains of Zelda's classroom. "Look what I found!" He blew ashes and soot off the object and then held it up for all to see. "It's a glass case with a bone inside. And it's not damaged! The glass didn't even melt."

"Well, Mrs. Sexton, I stand corrected," said Captain Plano. "Obviously not everything was destroyed in the fire after all." Turning to Phillips, the captain yelled, "Hey, Stan, bring it over here."

As the firefighter walked toward them, he announced, "The label says, 'Sacrum from an Egyptian princess, found in 1951 by Zelda Sexton.'"

Phillips tried to hand it over to Zelda. "Here you go, Mrs. Sexton."

Zelda froze. Her eyes grew wide with fear, and her lips began to quiver.

"Mrs. Sexton, this is for you."

"I don't want it!" she screeched. "I don't want to even touch it!" Zelda pleaded in a cracking voice. "I beg of you, destroy it! Get rid of it! Please, just get rid of it!"

And then she darted off, crying hysterically.

"Apparently your grandfather Stan, the firefighter, didn't destroy it," said Carter as he and Kyle stared at the bone in the glass case.

"Grandpa kept it," said Kyle. "I guess he thought your mom was upset because of the fire, and that's why she acted the way she did."

"Your grandfather had the sacrum for more than 40 years and nothing bad happened to him? No tragedies? No unexplained accidents? No bizarre incidents?"

"Just a normal life, nothing out of the ordinary. Why, did more bad things happen to your parents?"

"My mother was never the same after the fire. Her health declined, and she died seven years later. Dad became a sad and lonely man and lost interest in teaching. He was killed in a car accident in 1965."

"I'm sorry, Mr. Sexton."

"Kyle, please believe me. Now that I've touched the

sacrum, I'm convinced the Egyptian's spirit will be revived—because I'm the son of the woman who stole the bone. This is a dangerous spirit who was outraged at having her skeleton violated. She summoned up a vicious power to act through the bone and do terrible things to those connected with my mother. It's fortunate your grandfather was spared. We may not be so lucky. We can't take the chance. Do you understand?"

"Yes, sir."

Minutes later, Carter—armed with a hammer, a can of gasoline from the trunk of his car, and a lighter—and Kyle, who carried the bone, walked to a vacant lot behind the school. There, Carter cleared a small circular area and lined it with rocks. Then he smashed the bone to bits with the hammer, put them inside the circle of rocks, poured gasoline over them, and lit a fire. When the flames died out, he buried the ashes.

"That should put an end to the bone and the curse," declared Carter, wiping his hands.

"Mr. Sexton?"

"Yes?"

"She's not there now, but I saw a strange-looking young woman staring at us from the corner of the lot. She had a rounded hat, a gold necklace and gold bracelets, and a powder-blue dress. She reminded me of an Egyptian princess."

THE GHOSTLY FRIEND

Teacher Rick Hayden strode into his fifth-grade class wearing a top hat, white shirt, string tie, and black suit. He had a fake black beard, a big nose made out of putty, and a large mole on his cheek.

The students broke out in applause. Every month, Rick would dress up in costume and pretend to be a historical figure such as George Washington, Benjamin Franklin, or Paul Revere. Then he would conduct class as if he were that person and answer kids' questions in character. It made history so much more fun that way.

"Good morning, ladies and gentlemen," he announced. "I presume you know who stands before you."

"K-Mark, the Discount Magician," shouted Tim from the back of the room, cracking up the rest of the students.

"I know not of whom you speak," Rick replied. "However, it may take a magician to save your hide from being thrown into the stockade. Now again, I ask you, who am I?"

"Abraham Lincoln!" they shouted in unison.

Rick doffed his hat and bowed. "At your service." He pulled out a piece of paper and cleared his throat. "It is November 19, 1863, and I am in Gettysburg, Pennsylvania. I am standing at the site where a fierce battle raged four months ago between the Union and Confederate troops. The bloody conflict lasted three days and marked a turning point in the Civil War. General George Meade's Northern army battered Robert E. Lee's Southern force. More than 40,000 brave soldiers were injured or killed. I am here to deliver a speech at ceremonies dedicating the battlefield as a national cemetery for those who lost their lives."

Rick cleared his throat and repeated Lincoln's famous Gettysburg Address: "Four score and seven years ago our fathers brought forth upon this continent a new nation, conceived in liberty and dedicated to the proposition that all men are created equal. Now we are engaged—"

DING! . . . DING! . . . DING!

Darn it, Rick thought. *Not another fire alarm. Of all the times to have a fire drill. We just had one last week.* Annoyed, he took off his hat and beard. "Okay, kids, you know the drill. We've practiced it enough times. Single file. Let's go."

Rick opened the classroom door and was surprised to see one of his students, Bernie Goldman, already in the hallway. "Bernie, what are you doing out here?"

"Sorry, Mr. Hayden, I was late for school. My mom's car didn't want to start this morning."

"Okay, we're having another fire drill, so join the others."

The students streamed out of their classrooms and into the hall of Jackson Elementary. From there, they marched out of the doors and gathered on the playground behind the school.

Kids from the other classes giggled when they saw Rick Hayden's costume. They weren't surprised. They knew he was the school's coolest teacher, always willing to try zany things to make learning more interesting.

"Aren't your clothes a little out of style?" fourth-grade teacher Madelyn Keane kidded him. "Or are you trying to make a fashion statement?"

"Yes, these clothes are out of style, and yes, the statement I'm making is, thank goodness we don't have to dress up like this these days."

Principal Harold Tumway walked out to the playground, held up a megaphone, and said, "Everyone did an excellent job of evacuating the building in record time. Fortunately, there is no fire. It was a false alarm. You can return to your rooms now."

Before they began to move, however, a speeding car screeched around the corner and went into a skid. Now totally out of control, the car careened across the street and plowed through the bushes in front of the school. It then slammed into the building with such force that bricks and glass flew in all directions. The car finally came to a stop in the middle of a classroom—Rick Hayden's classroom.

"Stay here, kids!" Rick ordered. Then he and several other teachers dashed to the wrecked classroom. They shoved aside splintered desks and broken cement blocks to reach the smashed-up car. They pulled out the driver, an elderly man who, although badly shaken, had avoided serious injury thanks to his car's air bag and safety belt.

"I thought I was hitting the brakes," he mumbled. "I must have been stepping on the gas instead."

After other teachers escorted the driver to the school clinic, Rick and Mr. Tumway surveyed the damage in the room. Half the desks were busted and the front wall had collapsed.

"What a mess," groaned the principal.

"Mr. Tumway, if we hadn't had that fire drill, my students would have been right here in class. I would have been standing where the car is now. I shudder to think what could have happened. Some of my kids could have been killed."

"And you could have been too," said the principal. "Maybe I shouldn't be so angry over the fire drill."

"What do you mean?"

"Rick, it appears that someone—a student, no doubt—pulled the alarm. He or she should be found and punished. But yet this prank undoubtedly saved injury and possible death."

"Any idea who did it, Mr. Tumway?"

"No. But we do know that the alarm pulled was the one right outside your classroom. Were any of your students out of class at the time the alarm went off?"

"Yes. Bernie Goldman, the transfer student who joined us about a month ago. I saw him in the hall just as we were leaving the room. He told me he was late because his mom had car troubles."

"I think we should have a little talk with Bernie."

Rick hoped that Bernie hadn't done it because he liked him. The student, who had moved from California to Portland, Oregon, with his divorced mother at the start of second marking period, made friends quickly. He always had a compliment for everyone and enjoyed kidding around.

Bernie's eyes were big and gray like the color of a battleship. His ever-ready smile was kind of quirky—the left side of his mouth always seemed to be grinning. One of the reasons Rick liked Bernie was that the student's features reminded Rick of a good friend from childhood.

During lunch hour, Bernie was questioned by Mr. Tumway and Rick. Staring straight into their eyes, the student politely but steadfastly denied pulling the alarm. "I understand why you might suspect me," Bernie told them, "but I didn't do it."

"Do you know who did?" asked Rick.

For the first time during questioning, Bernie avoided making eye contact with them. He bowed his head. "I can't say."

"You *can't* say or you *won't* say?" asked Mr. Tumway, as he frowned and leaned toward the student.

"It's not what you think," Bernie replied, his voice beginning to squeak. "I don't know anything. Besides, shouldn't you be happy that the alarm went off? Who knows how many kids could have been killed otherwise."

"That's not the point, Bernie," said the principal. "Please don't hide anything from us. That makes you as guilty as the person who did it."

"It's not like I saw a student do it. Honest. It's no one."

Actually, it was someone—or rather something. But it would be several days before Rick Hayden learned the startling truth.

Rick loved teaching at Jackson Elementary because the faculty and administration were dedicated to making it the best school possible. He always had good feelings about it, because he used to attend Jackson when he was growing up. Back then, it was an eight-room building. But ten years earlier it had been remodeled and made much larger, with two dozen classrooms, a media center, gym, and cafeteria. Rick got a big kick out of teaching at Jackson because among his students were children of friends he had grown up with.

In the four years he had taught there, nothing unusual had ever happened—until the car crash. It would take two weeks for workers to repair the damage and get new desks in his classroom. During that time, Rick held class in the cafeteria.

It was difficult to teach his students there, especially around 11:30 A.M. when everyone was getting hungry and smelling the food cooking in the kitchen. But Rick made the most of it. Each day he'd pick a student to arrange the tables any way he or she wanted for class—into diamonds, rectangles, or circles.

One day, while Rick was teaching punctuation, Bernie raised his hand. "Mr. Hayden, it's stuffy in here. Could I open a window, please?"

"Sure, Bernie."

Bernie hurriedly opened several windows before a brisk

cold breeze blew papers off the table. "Bernie, please!" shouted Rick. "One window is okay. But not any more. We're getting blown away here—and it's cold."

Bernie paid no heed and continued to open all of the ten windows. "Bernie, did you hear me? Close them. Close all of them!"

Just then screams echoed off the cafeteria walls: "Get out! Hurry! Get out! Gas!" As the hacking and coughing kitchen employees rushed out the door, one of them yelled at Rick, "Get the kids out! Now!"

Rick quickly hustled the students out of the cafeteria. He soon learned that a new employee had accidentally mixed two cleaning liquids, causing a chemical reaction that triggered a dangerous gas.

After the bucket of cleansers had been removed and the cafeteria aired out, Mr. Tumway told Rick, "It was a good thing the windows were opened. The gas could have made you and your students very sick. Just out of curiosity, why were the windows opened in the first place? It's so chilly outside."

"Funny you should ask. Bernie Goldman asked to open a window, and then he furiously opened all of them right before the gas accident. It was like he knew."

At the end of the day, Rick asked Bernie to stay after class. "Bernie, did you have a premonition—a feeling in your gut—that there was going to be a gas hazard?"

"No, Mr. Hayden. I wanted some air, and I figured why not open all the windows so others could enjoy it."

"Bernie, tell me the truth."

"Okay. Caitlin called me a wimp because I said it was

cold in the room. You know how she is, never wearing a sweater or jacket in the winter. So I opened all the windows to freeze her out. I'm sorry, Mr. Hayden. But it turned out to be a lucky break, right?"

Rick nodded halfheartedly. He was convinced that Bernie was not telling the whole truth. But there was nothing more the teacher could say.

Rick's classroom was repaired just in time for the Jackson Open House, where parents and students would meet with the teachers on a one-to-one basis. Bernie and his mother, Maddy, were the last appointment of the night for Rick. While Bernie passed the time in the computer room next door, Rick talked with Bernie's mother.

"Bernie is a bright boy, Mrs. Goldman," said Rick. "For a new student, he's made quite a few friends."

"I was worried about him when I moved back to Portland," she said.

"Oh, you're from here? Bernie never mentioned that."

"I lived in Portland only a short time," Maddy explained. "I married Bernie's father here in 1983. But he was killed in an auto accident six months later. I was pregnant with Bernie, so I moved to California, where my folks live. About two years later I remarried, and my husband adopted Bernie. Unfortunately, we divorced last year. Then, when my company offered me a position back here, I decided to come. This may sound funny, but I wanted to be near my one true love—Peter."

"And Peter is?"

"Peter Lender, my first husband, Bernie's father. He's buried here in town."

"Peter Lender? I went to school with a Peter Lender. And he died in a car accident in the early 1980s! It has to be the same guy!" Then it dawned on Rick. "Bernie's gray eyes and that crooked smile—they reminded me of Peter!"

"I'm sorry, but I don't believe Peter ever mentioned you," said Maddy.

"We grew up together and attended Jackson Elementary. We were the best of friends. But then he moved to the other side of town, and we went to different schools and lost touch. I went off to college and taught in Iowa for several years. I didn't learn about Peter's death until a year after it happened. I didn't even know he was married. Imagine that. Bernie is Peter's son."

"It's a small world. Bernie thinks the world of you, Mr. Hayden."

"Well, I liked Bernie the minute I met him. Now I know why. He has Peter's genes."

Rick noticed a pained expression on Maddy's face. "What's wrong, Mrs. Goldman?"

"Bernie has been acting a little strange since we moved to Portland. He says he dreams about his real father. I've even heard him talking to Peter—well, obviously he talks to *himself,* not to Peter. And Bernie keeps asking questions about Peter. He insisted on having a photo of Peter in his room. He never did before."

"It's normal for a boy to wonder about his birth father. Bernie wasn't ready to ask those questions before. Now with the move to Portland, he's ready to learn as much as he can about Peter."

"I suppose you're right."

"Mrs. Goldman, did Bernie mention to you about why he opened all the cafeteria windows before the gas mishap, or if he had anything to do with the fire alarm right before the man crashed his car in my classroom?"

"No," she replied. "Why do you ask?"

"Never mind. Forget I even mentioned it."

"I certainly will," she snapped. "You make it sound like *he* had something to do with those incidents." She abruptly stood up and stormed out of the room. After she summoned Bernie from the computer room, the two walked past the teacher.

As Mrs. Goldman glared at the teacher, Bernie, who was not aware of any conflict, told him, "I locked the computer room, Mr. Hayden."

"Thank you, Bernie. Good night."

Rick returned to his desk to work on a lesson plan. But he couldn't concentrate. *Darn it, I never should have brought up those two incidents with Mrs. Goldman. That wasn't smart. Now I've angered her. Still, I can't help but wonder if Bernie wasn't somehow involved in both those accidents. I hope not. He's Peter's son, of all people.*

About ten minutes later Bernie entered the classroom. "Mr. Hayden, my mom's car won't start. Do you think you could take a look at it?"

"Of course, Bernie." The two went outside, where Rick tinkered with the engine. "It's a faulty starter switch, Mrs. Goldman. I think I can fix it to get you home, but you'll need to buy a new one."

"Thank you," she said curtly.

Just as the engine roared to life, Bernie tapped Rick on

the shoulder. "Mr. Hayden, you'd better check out the computer room. Um, I'm not so sure I locked it. Maybe you should go there."

Something in Bernie's voice made Rick believe there was cause for concern. The teacher hurried back inside. As he walked down the hallway, he noticed light coming from underneath the computer-room door. Then the light went off.

He reached the door and discovered it was unlocked. He quickly opened it and flipped on the light. Two figures ducked behind a desk. "Who's in here?" Rick said. No one answered. Then he noticed that two computers had been unplugged. The cords were wrapped around the monitors as if they were ready to be moved. "Whoever is in here better come out right now!"

Suddenly two high-school-age boys wearing black jackets and stocking caps pulled down low over their faces jumped up from behind a desk and rushed for the door. But before they could run past Rick, they both fell in a heap. They had been tripped up by a cord that mysteriously had been stretched across the aisle.

"*Ow*, my ankle," grimaced one of the teens.

The other boy was pressing his hand against his bloody forehead. "I think I busted my head. Willy, come on, let's make a run for it!"

"I can't, man. My ankle. I think I broke it. Besides, there are two of them."

"Huh?" said Rick. He turned around. There in the doorway stood Bernie. "Bernie, what are you doing here?"

"I don't know. I thought maybe you might need some help."

"Go to the hall phone and call 911. I think we have a couple of burglars here."

By the time police arrived, the teens had confessed to Rick that they had planned on stealing two computers and selling them. As the intruders were led away, Rick turned to Bernie, who was standing next to his mother, and asked, "Bernie, you didn't have anything to do with this, did you?"

"Oh, no, sir. I didn't. Honest."

Mrs. Goldman glared at the teacher and said, "How dare you suggest that my son was involved in a burglary?"

"Forgive me, Mrs. Goldman." Turning to her son, he asked, "I'm curious, Bernie, how did you know that there might be trouble?"

"I just . . . um . . . I don't know."

"Bernie, are you psychic?"

"Uh, no, sir. I just happened to be around at the right time, I guess. Just like you were a long time ago." Bernie covered his mouth, knowing he said something he wished he hadn't.

"Huh? What do you mean, Bernie?"

Mrs. Goldman grabbed Bernie by the arm. "Come on, Bernie, let's go. I don't like Mr. Hayden's questions. To think you would have anything to do with a burglary or that you are psychic. That's crazy!"

That night Rick couldn't sleep. He kept thinking about Bernie and Peter Lender. Rick dug out an old photo album and thumbed through it, looking for a picture of Peter. He soon found a photo of himself and Peter in Cub Scouts.

It's uncanny, he thought. *Bernie's eyes and smile are exactly the same as Peter's. They look so much alike.* Rick's mind drifted back to those carefree days when he and Peter were kids, always trying to outdo one another: Who could climb the tallest tree, dive off the highest part of a cliff into a water-filled quarry, soar the farthest off a bike ramp.

And then Rick thought about the time he had saved Peter's life when they were 12 years old. They had gone down to the river to swim. A rope had been tied to a sturdy branch of a tall oak on the bank. The boys swung from the rope far out over the water and then dropped into the river.

After about an hour of splashing into the water, Peter climbed past the branch holding the rope. At 40 feet (12 m) up, he shimmied his way out onto a branch until it began to bend.

"Come on up and join me, Ricky, or are you chicken?"

"I'm not chicken, Peter."

"Squawk! Squawk!" Peter replied, mockingly. All of a sudden the branch snapped. "Uh-oh." Peter was now dangling in the air, hanging on to the broken half of the branch.

"Hold on, Peter! I'll get you!"

It was too late. The broken branch twisted off, sending Peter crashing through the tree. To his horror, Rick saw Peter bang his head against another branch before plunging into the river.

Peter's unconscious body slapped the water before disappearing under the surface. Rick dove in and frantically swam in circles, searching for his best friend. "Peter! Peter!" he cried out. The water was too murky to see more than a couple of feet under the surface. Desperately, Rick paddled here and there, bobbing, diving, hoping against hope that he would find his friend. Suddenly, he felt Peter's arm. Rick pulled Peter up until his head was out of the water and dragged him to shore. There, Rick turned him on his side until water came out of Peter's mouth. Then Rick gave him mouth-to-mouth resuscitation.

Seconds later Peter began coughing as he slowly regained consciousness. He opened his eyes and then gagged, "Ricky, get your lips off me, man!"

"You're alive!"

"Of course I'm alive," Peter said between coughs, "although I don't feel so good. My lungs hurt and my head aches." Peter sat up and rested against the trunk of a tree. "Hey, thanks for saving my life. I'll never forget it."

"No sweat, man. You'd have done the same for me."

"I owe you big time. I'll pay you back someday."

That happened back in 1969, Rick recalled. *Peter died in 1983 when he was only 26 years old. What a shame he never got to see his son born.* Rick slammed the photo album shut. *Wait a minute! Could Bernie be Peter reincarnated? It has to be! Remember what Bernie said tonight? He said he happened to be around at the right time, "just like you were a long time ago." How could he possibly have known that I saved his father's life? His own mother didn't even know I was Peter's friend until tonight, and I didn't tell her about the near-drowning. This is amazing! This is incredible!*

The next day, after class, Rick questioned Bernie. "Last night you mentioned that I happened to be at the right place at the right time a long time ago. What did you mean by that?"

"Nothing, Mr. Hayden, nothing," answered Bernie, his

eyes growing wide from surprise. "It just slipped out. Can I go now?"

"Bernie, do you believe in reincarnation?"

"Mr. Hayden, I don't think you should be asking me a question like that. My mom would be really upset."

"I'm sorry, Bernie. You're right. It's just that you remind me so much of your father. We were good friends as kids. And I saved his life once. I know it sounds crazy, but I thought maybe you are really Peter reincarnated."

"You're way off, Mr. Hayden, way off!" Then Bernie, looking terribly frightened, rushed out of the room.

Rick pounded his desk in frustration. *What's the matter with me? How could I let my emotions cloud my judgment like that? I should know better than to discuss such things with a student. But if he's not Peter reincarnated, why is he always around when I'm about to face trouble?*

The next morning Bernie came to class early. "I'm sorry about yesterday, Mr. Hayden."

"You have nothing to be sorry about, Bernie. I was out of line. I apologize."

"I'm so confused, that's all. Things have been happening to me, and I'm trying to sort it all out. But this reincarnation stuff, you can forget about it. I'm positive I'm not my dad."

"How can you be so sure?"

Bernie hesitated for a moment before saying, "Because I've seen him."

The classroom door burst open, and several chattering kids filed into the room. Bernie immediately turned away from the teacher and walked over to his desk. Rick stared at him, not knowing what to say or think.

Throughout the morning in front of his class, Rick stumbled over his words, totally distracted by Bernie's astounding statement. The teacher couldn't wait to talk to him again alone. At recess Rick looked for Bernie and was told the student was last seen in the front of the school.

When Rick reached the front, he stopped and stared at a young man in his twenties with big gray eyes, curly black hair, and a crooked smile. The man, who stood about 100 yards (91.5 m) away, was waving at him.

No, it can't be, Rick thought. *I haven't seen him since the summer I graduated high school. But it has to be him.* Rick rubbed his eyes and looked again. "Peter? Peter Lender, is that you?" Rick shouted.

The man didn't say a word. He continued to wave, only this time more frantically. Terror filled his eyes, his mouth turned into a grimace.

"What?" shouted Rick. "You want me to move?"

Rick started walking toward him when he heard a loud splat behind him. A barrel of hot tar that workers were using to repair the school's roof had accidentally tipped over and fallen two stories off the ledge. The hot tar hit the ground right where Rick had been standing seconds earlier.

"Are you okay down there?" one of the workers hollered.

"Yeah, I'm fine," said Rick, extremely grateful that he hadn't been burned to death by the tar. When Rick turned around to look for the man who resembled Peter, he spotted Bernie standing in the man's place.

"Mr. Hayden, that was a close call."

"Bernie, where's the man who was standing here?"

"I didn't see anybody."

"You had to have seen him," Rick snapped. "He was right here just a few seconds ago." Rick grabbed Bernie by the shoulders. "Bernie, look at me. Now tell me the truth. Where is he?"

Tears welled up in Bernie's eyes. "He's gone."

"Who was he?"

"My dad," Bernie blurted. "I mean, his ghost."

Rick dropped his hands from the boy's shoulders. "That was Peter's ghost I saw just a moment ago?"

Bernie nodded. "I started seeing him shortly after my mom and I moved here. First, he was kind of ghostly, you know, like I could see through him. I thought I was dreaming or something. But then he started becoming clearer and clearer, and he talked to me and said he was my father. I thought I was going crazy. So I asked my mom for a picture of my real dad, and when she showed me, I knew it was him."

"Why didn't you tell me before?"

"It was supposed to be our secret. Besides, I just can't go around telling someone that I saw my father's ghost. Even you."

"But now I've seen him."

"He's been around the school for a while now. He stays close by to protect me—and you."

"Me?"

"Yes. He said you once saved his life, and he wanted to return the favor."

Rick walked back and forth, trying to let Bernie's astonishing words sink in.

"The fire alarm?" asked Rick.

"My father's ghost pulled it. I saw him do it when I was in the hallway. I didn't know why he pulled it at the time. But then we all saw what happened next. He saved a lot of lives—probably yours too."

"And you couldn't tell Mr. Tumway or me who really pulled the alarm without sounding crazy."

Bernie nodded. "Then in the cafeteria my father's ghost motioned me to open all the windows. It didn't make sense, but he looked very upset, so I opened all the windows."

"The gas accident, of course. Then did he tell you to alert me about the burglars in the computer room?"

"Yes. I saw him outside the school, pointing at the window to the computer room. Then he went into the room. He was the one who flicked on the light and scared the burglars. After you arrived, he tripped them when they tried to rush by you. They gave up when they saw you and him. He was behind you. When you turned around, I arrived, and my dad's ghost had gone."

Rick continued to walk back and forth. "So it was Peter's ghost who saved my life today by waving me away from the spot where the hot roofing tar fell."

"That's right, Mr. Hayden. I think he's paid you back a few times over for saving his life, don't you think?"

"Peter always said he would return the favor someday."

"I guess my dad was a man of his word—even after his death."

Time of Death

Myra Rivera brushed back the long, silky black hair from her face as she typed away at the computer. The popular 16-year-old student had taken a part-time job in the administration office of Buncombe High School because her father had been laid off from his job. She performed clerical duties for three hours every morning from 7 to 10 A.M. before attending classes the rest of the day.

When school secretary Faye Nelson entered the office, Myra looked up from her desk and said, "Good morning, Mrs. Nelson. There's a gold bracelet on your desk. I found it in the hall a few minutes ago."

"Thank you, Myra." Mrs. Nelson examined it closely. "This is definitely an expensive item. Thanks for turning it in."

"No thanks are necessary. I did what anybody would do."

"If only that were true. You're about as honest as they come, Myra."

After examining the bracelet with a magnifying glass, the secretary made a phone call. Then she walked over to Myra and handed her the bracelet. "It belongs to Miss Jennings. Would you please return it to her? She's in Room 308."

"Sure, Mrs. Nelson."

"Hmm," said the secretary. "Isn't 308 the homeroom of the coolest guy in school?"

Myra blushed. "I don't know who you're talking about," she replied with a wink.

"Scott Morris," said the secretary. "I understand he's quite a catch. I also understand he's going out with one of the prettiest girls in school. You still don't know who I'm talking about, hmm?"

Myra giggled. "Now that you mention it, I do seem to recall him." The truth was that Myra and Scott had been a twosome since the beginning of the school year. *This is great,* Myra thought. *I don't have to wait until the end of the day to see him. I'll write him a little note and try to slip it to him when I give Miss Jennings her bracelet.*

Myra took the valuable piece of jewelry and walked out of the office and into the looming halls of Buncombe High, the oldest school in the city. Opened in 1932, the building had awed tens of thousands of students over the years.

As Myra walked on the brown ceramic tile floor, she remembered how scared she had felt two years earlier during orientation for incoming freshmen. Buncombe High appeared so big, cold, and frightening. The thick cement block walls seemed better suited for prison cells than classrooms. The hallways were so high that the ceiling lights cast a dull, dreary light on the students below. The slamming lockers, dropped books, shuffling feet, and loud chatter echoed off the walls, making the corridors as noisy as traffic tunnels.

Despite all its faults, Buncombe High had something no other school in town had—a cherished history. Its legacy was so strong that members of the school board, all of whom had attended Buncombe when they were growing up, refused to consider closing the school.

The governor of the state had attended Buncombe. So had two major-league ballplayers, an NBA star, three Broadway actresses, and hundreds of doctors, lawyers, and public officials. There was no way they were going to tear this school down. It held too many fond memories.

Myra climbed the stairs to the third floor. Then something unusual happened. On her way to Room 308, she heard a woman crying in Room 303, the science lab. She knew there were no classes in that room this early in the morning. Curious, Myra pressed her ear against the door and listened. Someone definitely was sobbing.

What should I do? Myra wondered. *Maybe someone needs my help. Maybe it's a student with a personal problem who's found a place to be alone. Her crying sounds so heartbreaking. I've got to go check.*

Myra opened the door and stepped inside—and entered a bizarre world, a world where seeing was not necessarily believing.

Her eyes, ears, and nose immediately sent convincing

warning signals to the brain that nothing was normal and everything was strange.

A quick glance around the room left Myra totally baffled. There was no crying woman. More puzzling, the room no longer looked like the science lab. There were no lab counters with stools, no Bunsen burners, no glass tubes and jars of chemicals locked in huge cabinets. Instead, this room had rows of uncomfortable, straight-back wooden seats, each with a right-handed arm that flared out into a small square upon which to write.

As she cautiously walked toward the back of the room, Myra noticed the air—thick, stale, and almost stifling, as if in a closed-up attic. Her nose twitched from a strong musty odor, triggering a coughing fit.

Myra spotted two framed black and white photographic portraits hanging on the wall, each of a different smiling middle-aged man. At the bottom of each frame was a brass plate. One said "President Franklin Delano Roosevelt." The other said "Governor Cyrus Pickens." *Why are these photos here?* she wondered.

A hand-scrawled note pinned to a nearby bulletin board announced, "Hey, kiddos, don't forget the big dance Saturday night! Toots Bigelow and his Swing Band play the rowdiest, swellest music in town!"

Swing band? thought Myra. *What's a swing band?* Also pinned on the board was a newspaper headline that read: "Jesse Owens Wins Fourth Gold Medal." *Who's Jesse Owens?* Underneath it, a handwritten note in flowery penmanship said, "Mr. Owens believed in himself when no one else did and look what he accomplished. Set your sights high, and you too can win a gold medal in life!"

Thumbtacked next to a red and black Buncombe Bulldogs pennant was this neatly lettered sign in red paint: "Don't forget the BIG game against Central High! Bite 'em, Bulldogs!" *Bite 'em, Bulldogs? That's so lame! And where's Central High? I never heard of it before.*

It soon dawned on Myra that total silence had engulfed the room. She didn't hear a thing. She glanced at her watch. By now, on the P.A. system, Jill Repulski would be reading the morning announcements. A tardy kid or two would be making a mad dash to his or her homeroom. A media specialist would be pushing the overhead projector cart, its wheels making a clickety clackety sound down the hall.

But it was quiet—deathly quiet—in Room 303.

The silence finally was shattered by a woman's crying—the very reason Myra had entered the room. She turned toward the front. To Myra's surprise, a rail-thin woman was slumped over the teacher's desk, weeping. Her body heaved with every sob.

I can't tell who she is, thought Myra. *Her hair is funny, all piled up on top of her head, like an old-fashioned hairdo. I wonder who she is.*

"Are you, okay, Miss?" asked Myra.

The woman didn't respond. She continued to bawl. *She's obviously crying from heartache, not from pain,* Myra told herself. *I can't stand here like an idiot, I'd better do something. Maybe I should sneak out and leave her in peace. No, maybe I should go up and put my arms around her.*

But a slight fear was holding her back. Nothing made sense; neither the room, the silence, nor the strange woman.

Soon Myra's compassion overcame any misgivings. She crept forward, cleared her throat, and asked softly, "Pardon me, Miss, but can I help you?"

The woman ignored her. A half minute later, the woman sat up. For the first time Myra, who was ten feet (3 m) away, got a good look at her. The puzzled student had never seen her before.

The woman appeared to be in her early forties. The weeping had turned her pale blue eyes bloodshot and had flushed the cheeks on her otherwise milky white skin. She was wearing a long-sleeved white blouse with a lacy collar—the kind that women wore many years ago. She gently fingered an oversized green book with the face of a bulldog in bright yellow on the cover.

"I don't mean to bother you, Miss, but I heard you crying, so I came in to see if I could help," said Myra.

The woman continued to ignore Myra. She pulled a handkerchief out of her right sleeve and dabbed her wet eyes. "I don't want to leave," she whispered before her mouth twisted into another cry. She uttered the words with such sadness that it brought tears to Myra's eyes.

"Miss? Oh, Miss?" Myra said in a louder voice. When the student still received no recognition, she waved her arms to attract attention. Nothing. *The woman acts like I'm invisible. Obviously, she doesn't want me around. I guess I'd better go. Besides, this room gives me the creeps.*

As Myra started to walk away, a band struck up music, and young voices began singing, "For she's a jolly good fellow . . . for she's a jolly good fellow . . ."

What's going on? Myra walked over to the open window

and gazed outside. Down below on the front lawn of the school—known as the quad—about two dozen students in marching band uniforms were playing their instruments while hundreds of other singing students looked up at the window where Myra was standing.

What's wrong with this picture? she wondered. *The uniforms maybe? Our marching band wears snappy red and black uniforms with white-billed caps. These band members are wearing dorky black uniforms and funny red caps. And look at the students. The girls are wearing skirts below their calves! And the boys look ridiculous in their baggy pants and white socks and black shoes.*

Hey! Where's the shopping center across the street? Where's Rick's Deli? Berry's Record Shop? Cards 'n' Stuff? It's a vacant field! Youngman Avenue isn't a two-lane street that dead-ends just past the school. Why is there a baseball diamond where the gas station should be? Those cars in the street look so old—like from a gangster movie. Is this a movie set? Or is this what it's like when you lose your mind?

Myra closed her eyes, hoping that when she opened them, everything would return to normal; that the kids outside would have familiar faces, the shopping center would be across the street, and Youngman Avenue would be a busy four-laner that stretched for miles. She opened her eyes, but it remained the same weird scene from the past.

Nothing makes sense. I don't understand. Now Myra was beginning to panic. Shaking her head, she backed away from the window and then turned around. The sobbing woman was gone. "Miss? Where are you?" *This is too freaky for me. I've got to get out of here now!*

Myra bolted for the door and ran out into the hall. She began walking in a daze, her mind whirring with a million thoughts, none of which came close to explaining what she had just seen. She kept strolling aimlessly in the hall when . . . *Oh my gosh, what if I've stepped back in time? What if I'm trapped in a time warp? I've got to get back to the present!*

She glanced at her hand and noticed she was holding the bracelet she was supposed to return to Miss Jennings. *I forgot all about the bracelet. What if I go in her room and it's not the same? If Miss Jennings isn't there? If the class isn't there? If Scott isn't there? Oh no. Not Scott!*

Myra took a deep breath, closed her eyes, and with a quivering hand, opened the door to Room 308. *Oh, please, please, please be there, Miss Jennings.* She opened her eyes. *Oh, thank goodness! Thank goodness.* Myra leaned against the door jam and gave a big sigh of relief. *Yes, there's Miss Jennings!* Myra scanned the classroom. *There's Scott! I'm back in the present!*

"Myra, are you all right?" Miss Jennings asked. "You look terribly ill."

"I'm not feeling well, Miss Jennings," replied Myra, trying to calm herself. "But I feel a whole lot better than I did just a minute ago."

"Do you need to sit down? Do you need some water?"

"I'm not sure what I need. I'm just so shaky. Would you excuse me, please?" Somewhat fearfully, Myra walked over to the window and peeked outside. She smiled. There was Rick's and Berry's and the gas station.

"Myra, why are you looking outside?"

"I wanted to make sure everything was . . . uh . . ." *You can't tell her the real reason.* "Uh. I thought it was raining. It's not."

Several kids in the class began to laugh. Miss Jennings turned to Scott. "Scott, why don't you escort Myra to the school clinic."

"Sure, Miss Jennings," said Scott, popping out of his seat.

As he started to lead Myra out of the classroom, she turned to the teacher and said, "Oh, I almost forgot. Here's the bracelet you lost. Uh, I'm really glad you're here, Miss Jennings."

The teacher cocked her head and gave a quizzical smile. "Thank you, Myra. Now promise me you'll go straight to the clinic."

"Yes, the clinic. I will."

Myra clutched Scott's arm as they walked into the hall and then she burst into tears.

"Myra, what's wrong?" he asked.

"You'll think I'm stark raving mad if I tell you. And what's really scary is that I'm beginning to think I really am loony."

"Well, tell me anyway."

Myra described the crying woman, the changed science lab, and the outside scene from the past. To Scott, the story sounded so ridiculous, so unbelievable, that he didn't want to hear any more for fear that his girlfriend was mentally ill. But he also could tell from the look in her eyes that she was extremely frightened.

"Am I going crazy, Scott?"

"Why don't we take a look in Room 303, okay?"

"I don't want to go back in there."

"You don't have to, Myra. I'll go."

Myra put her ear to the door, wondering if she would hear the crying woman. But there was silence. She moved back until she was pressed against the opposite wall in the hall. "Go ahead, Scott," she said. "I'll stay out here."

Scott hesitated for a brief moment and then flung open the door. Gingerly, he stepped inside and looked around. He walked over to the window, took a glimpse outside, and then left the room, closing the door behind him.

"Well, what did you see?" Myra asked anxiously.

Scott put his arm around her shoulder. "Myra, I didn't see what you saw. The science lab looks the same. I didn't see anyone inside, and when I looked out the window, everything seemed normal."

Myra moaned and tears sprang up. "See? That proves it. I'm crazy!"

"It doesn't prove a thing, Myra. You're far from crazy. You're the most sane person I've ever met in my life. There's an explanation for this."

"But what is it?"

Scott answered by shaking his head and shrugging.

"Scott, you positively, absolutely can't tell anyone about this."

"Okay, Myra, I won't. What are you going to say to the school nurse?"

"I'll tell her I'm coming down with the flu."

"We have to figure this out, Myra. Meet me after class in the school library. We'll launch our own investigation."

No matter how hard Myra tried to shove the experience out of her mind, she couldn't—not an incident this astounding. She was so obviously distracted that teachers in each of her classes asked her, "What's the matter?" She put on a fake smile and replied, "Nothing."

After the final period she met Scott in the school library, where he had already gathered several books.

"Look at this," he said, pointing to a chronicle of United States history. "I think I've pinpointed the year. You mentioned you saw a newspaper clipping of Jesse Owens. He was a great African-American track star who won four gold medals in the 1936 Olympics in Berlin, Germany. He really showed up Adolf Hitler, the Nazi dictator, who thought blacks were inferior.

"Also, you said there were pictures of Governor Pickens and President Roosevelt. Well, they both held office in 1936. Does that year mean anything to you? Maybe you read about it, and it stuck in your mind?"

"A total blank, Scott. The year means nothing to me."

Scott pushed another book in front of Myra. It was a pictorial year-by-year almanac. He flipped the pages to the 1930s. "Look at these cars and the way people dressed. Is this what you saw when you looked out the window?"

"Yes!" she cried out. "Yes! Those are the same kinds of cars I saw. And the clothes. Scott, do you think I entered a time warp?"

"That's pretty far-fetched, Myra, but who knows?"

"So who was the woman? And why would students be singing, 'For she's a jolly good fellow'?" Myra snapped her fingers. "The yearbook, of course!" She soon found the aisle where the entire collection of the *Buncombe Barker* was shelved. Each book had its own distinctive design and color. "There it is, the 1936 *Buncombe Barker!*" she whispered excitedly.

She pulled it out and then clutched Scott's arm. "This looks exactly like the book the woman was holding when I saw her. It's the same size, and the cover was green and had a yellow bulldog on it just like this."

She plopped to the floor with the book on her knees and began flipping slowly through the pages. "I got a good look at her. If she's a teacher, I should find her in here."

She turned the first few pages and then stopped, stabbing her finger at a full-page photo. It was shot from a third-floor window, down onto the quad where students had gathered for a rally. "Look at this photo, Scott. What do you see across the street?"

"Nothing but a baseball diamond."

"Right! That's what I saw from virtually the same vantage point in Room 303!" Myra's heart was beating faster. Each new clue boosted her confidence that she wasn't crazy. But each new clue only added to the mystery.

Trying hard to stay calm, she continued to flip through the pages until she reached a section on the teachers. She took a deep breath and said, "Well, here goes." Her eyes carefully scanned the English teachers, the math teachers, and then the science teachers.

Moments later she sucked in air and threw her left hand over her mouth. Pointing with her right hand to the photo of a middle-aged woman, Myra exclaimed, "That's her! That's the teacher I saw crying in the room!" She read the caption.

"Her name is Clara Mills. My gosh, Scott, I saw Clara Mills's ghost!"

"Is there anything else about her?" asked Scott.

Myra thumbed through the index and found two other references for Miss Mills. Page 42 showed a photo of her with members of the Science Club. Page 65 featured the results of a poll. Students had voted on an assortment of subjects from "favorite tune" to "favorite gathering place." Miss Mills had been chosen "favorite teacher."

"This is starting to make a little sense," said Myra. "Miss Mills was a science teacher. I saw her in the science lab even though it didn't look like one. And since she was the students' favorite teacher, that could explain why the kids were singing 'For she's a jolly good fellow.'"

"Unfortunately, it doesn't explain the big questions. Why did you see her in the first place? And why did everything look like it was back in time?"

"Maybe we'll learn more about her by looking at other yearbooks." They discovered that every year since the school opened in 1932, Miss Mills had been voted "favorite teacher."

"Do you notice anything different about her photos from 1932 to 1936?" Scott asked.

"She got a lot thinner."

"Right. See how healthy she looks in 1932? By 1936 she's nothing but skin and bones. I bet you she lost 30 or 40 pounds."

Myra pulled out the 1937 yearbook, which had only one mention of Miss Mills. It was on page 1.

Myra turned to the page and blurted, "Oh, Scott, no!"

In the center of the page, bordered in black, was a photo of Miss Mills. Below were the words:

> IN MEMORIAM
> "FAVORITE TEACHER OF THE YEAR"
> CLARA MILLS
> 1895-1936
>
> The 1935-36 school year ended on a tragic note when Clara Mills, who was voted "favorite teacher" every year since Buncombe High opened its doors, died of heart failure in her classroom on the final day of school.
>
> Miss Mills had planned to retire because of failing health. A special surprise ceremony was to be held for her but, sadly, she died minutes before it began.
>
> Miss Mills was much loved and will be sorely missed.
>
> This yearbook is dedicated in her memory.

"Do you believe this?" Myra exclaimed. "I must have seen Miss Mills right before she died!"

"You mean, 60 years *after* she died," Scott reminded her. "You saw her today."

"Do you suppose we could find someone who remembers her?"

"Let's try the school board," he said. "All of the members

used to be students here at Buncombe High."

After doing a little research, they discovered that one of the board members, Lyndon Farwell, attended Buncombe High in 1936. Unable to take the yearbook home with them, the two teens made a photocopy of a page containing Miss Mills's photo. Then they visited the home of Mr. Farwell and showed him the picture.

"Do you remember Miss Mills?" Myra asked the 74-year-old board member.

"I surely do," replied Mr. Farwell. "I had her for only one year, 1936, when I was a freshman. What a wonderful teacher she was. Bright and cheery. She taught us much more than science. She taught us the power of positive thinking. She convinced every one of us that we could achieve great things, that anything was possible if we believed in ourselves. She motivated us and challenged us and made us not only better students but better people. Everyone loved her."

"What happened to her?" asked Scott.

"She had cancer. But her spirit was strong, and she never talked about her illness. She lived to teach. When I had her for a teacher, she was ailing pretty badly. But she refused to rest or take time off. She kept teaching. It was her way of staying alive. She made it all the way to the end of the school year."

Tears began welling up in the old man's eyes. "I'll never forget her final day. We students had signed a yearbook especially for her. In fact, one of the teachers found former students who had graduated and got them to sign it too. We were going to present it to her on the last day of school as a surprise.

"We gathered outside on the quad, and the band was playing, and we were singing, 'For she's a jolly good fellow.' She was supposed to come to the window. But she never came. One of the teachers went to get her, and he found her slumped over her desk, dead. I can't begin to tell you the shock and hurt we felt when we learned she had died. The kids walked around in a stupor."

"The yearbook," said Myra. "Did you give her the yearbook?"

"I'm sorry to say we didn't. We had it outside to give to her at the ceremony but by then she was dead. She had no family. So they decided to keep it in her classroom. Someone built a cabinet, and the signed yearbook was placed there for posterity, you know, as a remembrance to her."

"But," said Scott, "it's not there now."

"It's been so long," said Mr. Farwell. "Sadly, at some point over the years, probably during one of the school's many remodeling phases, the cabinet and book were removed because no one knew any better."

Scott stared at Myra and murmured, "Looks like we've hit a dead end."

"I guess you're right," she sighed.

"I wish you could find the yearbook that all of us students signed," said Mr. Farwell. "It was a wonderful testament to a wonderful teacher."

"We don't know where else to look."

Mr. Farwell paused a minute. "Say, I just thought of someone you should see. Guido Foggia. He was the janitor at Buncombe for about 40 years. He retired many years ago. Maybe he knows what happened to it."

Later that day, they visited Mr. Foggia, a spry 86-year-old, who proudly told them he still walked a mile around the neighborhood every morning and read at least one book a week. "So what brings you young folks to my doorstep?" he asked.

When they explained their reason for seeing him, his mouth dropped at the mention of Miss Mills's name. "This is so spooky! I saw her two days ago!"

Scott held up Miss Mills's photo. "You saw this Miss Mills two days ago?" he asked in a disbelieving voice.

"I'm old, but I'm not senile. I know what I'm saying. Yes, it's the same Miss Mills in your photo."

"But how?"

"The other day, out of the blue, I came back from my walk and there she was—as lifelike as can be. I thought I was having a stroke. But she truly appeared to me. Well, I guess it wasn't her, but her ghost. She looked so real. All she said was, 'I've come for my yearbook.'

"I knew immediately what she was after—the yearbook that everyone had signed. It had been kept in a special cabinet for years. When the school was remodeled in 1960, the cabinet was removed and got accidentally busted. I rescued the yearbook and brought it home for safekeeping. They were supposed to find a new place for it, but somehow we all forgot about it. For years it stayed in my bookcase along with all the other yearbooks I had from 1932 to 1975, when I retired as the school's chief maintenance man. There's a nice story and picture of me in the 1975 yearbook."

"Let's get back to Miss Mills's ghost," Myra said.

"After she mentioned the yearbook, she just disappeared. I pinched myself real hard to see if I was awake. I was. So I go over to the bookcase and—if I'm lying, I'm dying—the yearbook is gone!"

"Gone?" Scott exclaimed.

"Gone. You can see the space between the books on either side where it used to sit on the shelf. Go figure."

"Mr. Foggia," said Myra, "I'm going to reveal something that I haven't told anyone except for Scott. I saw Miss Mills too." Myra then described her stunning experience in the science lab. "When I last saw her, Miss Mills was holding the 1936 yearbook!"

Mr. Foggia grunted knowingly. "You know what I think? Miss Mills's spirit had been searching for that yearbook for years. When she found it, she returned to her room—the one place she loved the most. This time, she got to read all the marvelous comments written about her in the yearbook. That's why she was crying."

"Why did I see and hear things from 1936?" asked Myra.

"It was probably the most intense moment of Clara Mills's life. Her ghost was reliving the moment when you walked into the room. You unknowingly tapped into her ghost's memory."

"I get it," said Myra. "But now it's become my memory too—one I will carry for the rest of my life."

Dead Man's Shadow

The horrible vision appeared without warning.

Sixth-grade teacher Mike Kerr was discussing grammar with his class when he developed a headache. It started out as a dull pain in the back of his neck and crept its way up and over his skull before sliding down his forehead.

Suddenly an image began to appear in his mind. Gradually it came into focus until he saw in vivid and frightening detail the anguished face of a bearded man—a man hanging from a rope around his neck!

Mike closed his eyes, but the appalling mental picture remained as clear as if he were staring at the man in real life. The vision lasted about ten seconds before it faded away, leaving Mike so jolted that he had to lean against his desk to keep from falling.

"Mr. Kerr, Mr. Kerr," called out Stacy Reingold, one of his students. "Are you all right?"

"I'm sorry, class," mumbled the teacher. "I'm not feeling well. I have a splitting headache. Uh, turn to chapter 10 and start reading. I'll be right back."

He staggered to the bathroom, looked in the mirror, and saw that all the color had gone out of his cheeks. He splashed cold water on his face and shook his head. *What was that all about?* he wondered. *What just happened to me?*

Mike Kerr was enjoying his first year of teaching sixth grade at Reynolds Elementary. It was challenging but rewarding because he had a good group of students. Besides, he was living in his favorite locale—in the beautiful foothills of Virginia. His parents had been raised there before they moved to Massachusetts, where Mike grew up.

By early spring Mike had become one of the most popular teachers in school. Shortly before his thirtieth birthday, he joked with his students that they should shower him with gifts—ones that cost no money—to cheer him up because he was starting to feel "old."

On the morning of Mike's birthday, student Todd Fisher arrived in school with what he thought was a great present for his teacher. Todd wasn't the best student; he was lucky if he pulled B's and C's. He tried—maybe not hard enough—but at least he made an effort. He was a good kid who stayed out of trouble and displayed a great sense of humor.

"Here, Mr. Kerr, this is for you," said Todd, beaming. Then he placed an old, chipped, dusty brick on the teacher's desk. "Happy birthday."

"Thank you, Todd," said Mike, as he picked up the brick. "Um, what is it?"

"It's a brick."

"Yes, I know it's a brick. Does it have any significance? Or does this symbolize my effectiveness as a teacher?"

"Yes, uh, I mean no. What I'm trying to say is, it does have some significance. My dad owns a demolition company, and this brick comes from the very first schoolhouse here in Rockton. My dad tore it down last year. I thought maybe since your kinfolk probably went to that school, you'd like to have a brick from it. Maybe use it as a paperweight or something. I took one for myself and keep it in my room."

Mike lifted the brick and turned it gently in his hand. He looked at Todd and smiled. "This is a wonderful gift, Todd. Thanks. I'll keep it here on my desk to hold down all the A-plus homework I'll be getting from you."

"A feather paperweight would work just as well for the number of A's I get in homework."

Mike laughed and gently placed the brick near one corner of his desk.

Other students brought their teacher presents, including homemade cookies and a set of baseball cards. It seemed like it was going to be a wonderful birthday—until the vision appeared.

Mike tried to forget about it. But he couldn't. That's because the same headache, followed by the same intense vision, struck him every day for a week. It would hit without warning, while working a math problem on the blackboard, or calling on a student, or inserting a video in the VCR for a science film. Day after day, the mental snapshot would flash in his brain, remain for several seconds, and then vanish.

Mike needed all the concentration he could muster to get him through each day without cracking. But the strain was beginning to show. *I don't get it,* he told himself. *I'm not under any stress. I'm in excellent health. So why am I getting headaches? Why this particular vision? What does it mean? How do I make it stay away?*

Mike was in the middle of an astronomy lesson when the latest vision appeared. "Excuse me, class," he said, turning away from them so they wouldn't see him grimace. Once the vision faded away, he faced the students again.

"Now then, where was I? Oh, yes, who can name, in order, the two planets between the earth and the sun? Todd?"

"What, me?" squeaked Todd. Mike noticed a look of sheer terror spreading across the student's face. The boy gulped and broke out into a cold sweat. Now this was not a difficult question. Even if it was, it shouldn't have caused such a reaction in Todd. "Todd, are you all right?" asked the teacher.

"Mr. Kerr, I don't feel well. May I be excused so I can go to the bathroom?"

"Sure, Todd."

At the end of the day, Mike asked Todd to stay after class. "Is something wrong, Todd? I've noticed these last few days that you seem, well, preoccupied. Is something on your mind? Is everything okay at home?"

"Things are cool at home, Mr. Kerr. I guess I must be coming down with the flu. I've been getting a lot of headaches lately."

"Me too, Todd. Still, you looked scared today when I

asked you a question in class. That's not like you, even when you don't know the answer."

Todd lowered his head and didn't say a word. His eyes welled up with tears. "Mr. Kerr, I think I need some help. I think I'm sick in the head."

Mike led the student to a desk, and they both sat down. "What's wrong, Todd?"

"I've been seeing things in my mind—bad things. Every day a picture pops into my mind. It's awful. It's of a man hanging from a rope by his neck."

Mike sat stunned. *This is incredible. Poor Todd is seeing it too.* The teacher leaned forward and asked, "Did this man have a beard?"

"Yes, he did. How did you know that?"

"I'm not sure." *Don't reveal too much yet,* Mike told himself. *You don't want to scare Todd. His vision and mine must be connected in some manner. I wonder if other kids in the class are seeing the same thing, although they don't act like they do.*

"Am I going crazy, Mr. Kerr?"

"No, Todd. There has to be an explanation. I'll help you get to the bottom of this."

"You won't tell anyone, will you? Otherwise, they'll think I'm nuts."

"I'll keep it quiet. When did you first start seeing the vision?"

"About a week ago."

That's when mine started, thought Mike. *What's the connection?* "Todd, did anything happen back then, anything unusual you can recall?"

"No. Baseball practice started, but I didn't get hit in the head with a ball or anything like that."

Mike walked over to his desk and looked at his calendar for the previous week. He picked up the brick and moved it to get a better look. Teachers' meeting on Monday night. Basketball Tuesday night. Birthday on Wednesday. Date with Jan on Friday night. "Todd, try to remember exactly when you first saw the vision."

"I was riding my bike home from my dad's office. I had stuffed a couple of bricks from the old school in my backpack when I first saw that man in my mind."

Mike looked back at his calendar. *The brick! Todd gave me a brick the next day on my birthday—the day I first started seeing that terrible image!*

"Todd, let me investigate this matter. I don't understand why you should suffer from this vision, but I promise to try to put an end to it."

"Thanks, Mr. Kerr. I don't want to see this man anymore. He's too scary."

After Todd left, Mike picked up the brick and held it in his hand. He examined all six sides as flecks of red chips and dust came off in his hands. The side that had been exposed to the elements had several coats of paint on it. For an instant, Mike thought that side felt warmer than the others, as if it was giving off energy.

Suddenly, like a bolt, Mike was hit again with the vision of the hanged man. This time it was more intense than ever. The man's bloodshot eyes seemed so big and full of terror, anger, and despair. The image remained seared in his mind several seconds longer than usual. It didn't start to fade until Mike let go of the brick, which then fell with a thud on top of his desk.

"It's got to be the brick!" Mike exclaimed to himself.

He drove straight to Fisher Demolition, the firm owned by Todd's dad, Harvey. Mike had no idea what he was going to say or learn. He just knew he needed to go there.

After exchanging pleasantries with Harvey in the company office, Mike told him, "Your son was thoughtful enough to give me a birthday present—a brick from the old schoolhouse you tore down."

"That's my boy. Always trying to butter up the teacher," Harvey said with a laugh. "I'm just joshing you, Mr. Kerr. So, what do you want, more bricks?"

"No, I'd like some information. Were the bricks used for anything after the school was torn down?"

"No, we just dumped them out back for use later as fill. Some people who had gone to that school took a brick as a memento. I probably should have sold the bricks to them, but what the heck, I'm a nice guy."

"This is going to sound really weird, Mr. Fisher, but I was wondering if there's any kind of link between the bricks from the schoolhouse and the hanging of a man."

"Well, there sure as shooting was."

"What?" Mike gasped, squeezing the arm of his chair. "There was?"

"Yep. Haven't you heard about the dead man's shadow?"

Mike shook his head.

"Gosh, everybody in town knows about that. It's the strangest thing that's ever happened here in Rockton. And you didn't know, huh? I guess because you're kind of new to the area, although you have kin who were raised here and—"

"Mr. Fisher, please," interrupted Mike. "I've got to know. What's the story?"

"Let's grab us a soda and sit outside a spell, and I'll tell you all about the dead man's shadow."

In 1875, Del Kincaid, a bearded husky mountain of a man, became the area's first male teacher. The men in town couldn't figure out why this burly, 6-foot 4-inch (2-m), 220-pound (100-kg) former lumberjack would want to be a schoolteacher. But they didn't dare kid him to his face because Kincaid had a quick temper and wasn't afraid to unleash it.

In school he demanded the kids sit up in their chairs, address him as "sir," stay quiet in class, and do all their homework. He wouldn't put up with any antics or excuses. If they behaved, he rewarded them with extra playtime and cookies that his girlfriend would make. If they misbehaved, he made them stand in the corner for an hour. If they were really bad, he ordered them to clean the outhouse behind the school.

Only one boy, Randall Turnipseed, ever received the outhouse punishment—twice. He and Kincaid were at odds throughout the youth's years in school. The two never got along. Randall complained that the teacher "had it in for me from the get-go." Kincaid claimed that the boy was "incorrigible—a disruptive influence on the others."

For the most part, the parents liked Kincaid and the job he was doing instructing their children. And the kids respected him.

Over summer vacation in 1880, the teacher took a job helping the local blacksmith. One day, a miner named Tom Worthy—one of the roughest men in town—complained to Kincaid about the job he did shoeing Tom's horse. One word led to another and Worthy, who was about Kincaid's size, sucker-punched the teacher, knocking him down. Kincaid got up, but when he noticed that two of his students outside were watching him, he put down his fists and dusted himself off.

Clearly the teacher was fuming mad, but he held his anger because of the boys. Turning to them, he said, "Fighting might end a conversation, but it doesn't solve anything. I will resolve this matter my way. Now, go on, boys. Scat!"

Worthy never returned home; only his horse did. That evening, his family went searching for him. They discovered his body shortly before sunset, lying by a bridge. He had been stabbed with his own knife. Although Worthy had several enemies, suspicion immediately fell on Kincaid.

Sheriff Wiley Boone, a close friend of Worthy's, went to the teacher's house later that night and roused him out of bed to question him. Kincaid denied any knowledge of Worthy's murder, but Boone didn't believe him—especially when the sheriff noticed bloodstains on a shirt that was draped over the chair.

"Del, where were you between 6 P.M. and 9 P.M.?"

"After work, I went rabbit hunting and then came home," the teacher replied.

"Where did you get the bloodstains on your shirt?"

"From cleaning the rabbit I caught."

"Where's the rabbit?"

"I ate it."

The sheriff was convinced that Kincaid had committed the crime, but he still didn't have enough evidence—until a witness stepped forward. Randall Turnipseed, the boy who couldn't stand Kincaid, walked into the sheriff's office the next day and said, "I heard about the murder, sir. I know who killed Tom Worthy!"

"Well, spit it out, boy. Who's the killer?"

"Mr. Del Kincaid."

"How do you know that?"

"Last night, I was out coon hunting, and I saw Mr. Kincaid and Mr. Worthy arguing by the bridge. The two began wrestling, and the next thing I know, Mr. Worthy is sprawled by the side of the road, dead."

"Why didn't you come forward last night, boy?"

"I thought Mr. Kincaid saw me, and I was afraid he'd come after me."

Sheriff Boone and a deputy marched over to the blacksmith's shop where Kincaid was working. "Del," Boone said, "you're under arrest for the murder of Tom Worthy."

"I told you I didn't do it."

"We have a witness. Now are you going to come peacefully?"

"Yes, I have nothing to hide."

Kincaid was locked in jail while the sheriff tried to piece together the evidence needed to prove that the teacher was the murderer. Day after day, Sheriff Boone questioned Kincaid, trying to coax a confession. But Kincaid would angrily reply, "I haven't killed anyone, and whoever says

I did will have to face the consequences of the truth."

A few weeks later Kincaid was brought to trial. Witnesses described instances where they saw the teacher's temper, which in the excitement of a murder trial, became greatly exaggerated. Then his boss and two of his own students described the scene that took place when Tom Worthy knocked Kincaid down.

Next, Randall Turnipseed took the stand. He described in detail how Kincaid had waited for Worthy by the bridge and then ambushed him. In the course of the fight, said the boy, Kincaid grabbed Worthy's knife and stabbed him several times. Some of Randall's testimony didn't match the evidence.

First, Worthy had been stabbed only once. For the murder to have happened at 8 P.M., as Randall claimed, Kincaid, who left the blacksmith's at seven-thirty, would have had to gallop his horse for nearly thirty minutes in order to reach the bridge, yet no witnesses saw him gallop out of town. Also, Randall was known to tell tall tales. Even though the judge suspected the boy was probably not all that truthful, the testimony was allowed to stand.

Finally, Sheriff Boone took the stand and held up the bloody shirt that Kincaid was wearing the night of the murder. "This clinches it for me. The man is guilty, plain and simple, of murdering my friend, who was a decent father and good husband."

After the state presented its case, Kincaid testified on his own behalf. "Yes, I had words with Tom Worthy the afternoon of his death. Yes, he punched me. But other men in town have traded words and fists with Tom at one time or another. Any one of them could have had a score to settle. And although I disliked the man, I certainly didn't want to see him dead."

He gazed around the courtroom and continued. "After work, I went rabbit hunting nowhere near where Tom was killed. And then I went home. I did not murder Tom Worthy—and that's the truth!" His voice rang full and sharp; his eyes blazed with fervor.

The prosecutor wasn't swayed. In his closing argument, the attorney faced the men in the jury box. (Women were not permitted to serve on juries back then.) "Gentlemen of the jury, it's obvious who killed Tom Worthy. We have a motive—a man who seeks revenge after being humiliated in front of his own students. We have a witness—a boy who saw the murder with his own eyes. And we have physical evidence—a bloody shirt. Can there be any doubt in your mind who committed this crime? In the name of all that's decent, in the name of the victim, I implore you to find Del Kincaid guilty of murder."

The jury took less than an hour to reach its verdict. After the twelve men returned to the courtroom, Kincaid stood at the defendant's table and stared at them. Then he held his breath as the jury foreman said, "We, the jury, find the prisoner, Del Kincaid, guilty of the murder whereof he stands charged."

A shudder rippled through Kincaid's massive body, and his lips quivered in disbelief. Members of the audience broke out in shouts, causing the judge to rap his gavel sharply.

The judge turned to Kincaid and asked, "Have you anything to say before I pronounce the sentencing?"

"Yes, your honor," replied Kincaid, his neck muscles straining from anger. Staring at the faces of the witnesses who testified against him, he bellowed, "I have not killed anybody. Those who say I did are liars. I will haunt this town until each and every liar takes his final breath." Kincaid slumped back in his chair.

The judge cleared his throat and said, "It is the judgment of this court that the prisoner, Del Kincaid, be sentenced to death. He is to be remanded to the Common Jail of this county and there remain until the twenty-first day of August, whereupon he is to be taken by Sheriff Boone from the jail to the place of execution between the hours of ten o'clock in the morning and two o'clock in the afternoon, and there be hanged by the neck until dead. It is also the order of the court that all of Del Kincaid's property be sold at auction to help pay for the cost of this trial. Court is adjourned."

Kincaid kept shaking his head in protest as he was led away by the deputies to await his doom.

On the day of Kincaid's execution, buggies and wagons full of families from neighboring towns and counties began arriving in Rockton. They had come to watch the murderer hang.

When Sheriff Boone went to Kincaid's cell to escort him to the gallows, the lawman was surprised at how calm the condemned man acted. "It's time, Del," said the sheriff. "You're not going to give me any trouble today, are you?"

"No, Sheriff. I've never given you cause."

"Well, you don't seem as upset as I'd expect of a man about to be hanged."

"Oh, I'm plenty upset, Sheriff. And I intend to let everyone know that I've been falsely accused."

Moments later Kincaid sat between the sheriff and a deputy in a horse-drawn wagon that slowly rolled through the throng of onlookers. Kincaid remained expressionless, tuning out the jeers and comments from the crowd.

A few hundred yards ahead in the town square stood the wooden gallows that had been built solely for Kincaid's execution. With his hands tied behind his back, Kincaid was led to the top of the platform. He looked around at the huge crowd that had gathered to see him die. Then he gazed across the street at the red brick schoolhouse—the building that had brought him so much satisfaction as a teacher. *It should never have come to this,* he thought. *I should be in that schoolhouse, teaching, not facing my death. I belong in the classroom. How can they do this to me?*

"Do you have any last words?" the sheriff asked him.

"Yes," he said quietly. Turning toward the crowd, he shouted, "I am an innocent man—and my soul will not rest. It shall find a way to prove to this town that I'm going blameless to the gallows." Tears trickled down his face, causing his beard to glisten in the hot afternoon sun.

Sheriff Boone then placed a black hood over Kincaid's head, slipped the noose around his neck, and tightened it. At exactly 1 P.M., Del Kincaid was hanged.

Satisfied that justice had been done, members of the crowd went their separate ways, leaving the town square empty. Randall Turnipseed was one of the last to leave the area. He watched as the deputies lowered the body of his former teacher and placed it on the horse-drawn wagon.

Randall started to walk away when he glanced at the schoolhouse. Suddenly he felt sick to his stomach. He blinked once, then again and again. *No, it can't be!* he thought. *It must be my imagination!*

There on the south side of the schoolhouse wall—the one facing the gallows—loomed a mysterious shadow. It was the unmistakable, life-sized form of a burly, bearded man hanging from a rope by his neck!

Randall closed his eyes and rubbed them. When he opened them, he saw the same eerie scene. Although faint enough that it could easily be missed by passersby, it was clear enough to anyone who looked at it closely.

Randall walked several yards to his left and then several yards to his right, trying to study the shadow from different angles. But it looked the same no matter where he stood. He grabbed the arm of a friend who had been walking by.

"Henry, look!" Randall said, pointing to the south wall. "What do you see?"

"The schoolhouse."

"No, look at the wall. The shadow."

Henry gave a whistle and gasped, "It looks like a shadow of the hanging!" Turning to several other passersby, Henry shouted, "Hey, everybody, look at the shadow on the wall!"

A murmur spread throughout the town square. People spilled out of the stores and buildings; buggies turned around; men on horseback galloped back. Within an hour the square was once again thick with people buzzing about the strange sight.

"It's a haunting!"

"It's Kincaid, all right. It would take a man as large as him to cast such a big shadow."

"That Kincaid fellow is getting his revenge on us."

"No. Del is telling us he's innocent."

"Maybe it's an illusion."

As night fell, the shadow disappeared. But to everyone's astonishment, it returned at daybreak—and stayed all day. Sheriff Boone immediately tore down the gallows, but that had no effect on the shadow. In fact, nothing did. It appeared every day—rain or shine—on the side of the brick wall.

Men, women, and children from miles around flocked to Rockton to see the bizarre dead man's shadow. Sheriff Boone, the mayor, and many other townspeople were upset and embarrassed by the spectacle. "We can't expect our children to attend a school with the shadow of a dead man on it," said the mayor.

Volunteers tried to scrub the shadow off the red brick wall. When that failed, they tried to cover it up with white paint. But the shadow remained. Then they tried painting the wall black. It still did no good. The shadow showed up as a lighter shade of gray. Finally, with the new school year rapidly approaching, officials came up with the solution. They transplanted ivy from the homes of several volunteers and covered up the entire south wall. That way, the dead man's shadow could no longer be seen.

"I'm blown away by this story, Mr. Fisher," Mike blurted. His hand was shaking so much he couldn't finish his drink. "Are you sure this Del Kincaid had a beard?"

"That's what they say."

"So what happened when you tore down the school? Did you see the shadow?"

"No, we didn't. But you're getting ahead of me. You see, there's more to the story. You know how kids can be. Even though the ivy covered up the wall, every year or so, kids would strip the ivy and get a glimpse of the shadow. This went on for years.

"But then when the kids pulled the ivy down one day back in 1898, the shadow was plum gone. It had disappeared, and it never came back."

"Why?" asked Mike.

"I'll tell you what I think. Remember Randall Turnipseed, the boy whose testimony hung Del Kincaid? Well, after he grew up, he fought in the Spanish-American War in 1898 and was seriously wounded. He was brought back to Rockton, but he never recovered. On his death bed, he gave a confession. He said that he never saw Del Kincaid at the bridge. In fact, Randall wasn't anywhere close to the murder scene. He had been sore at his old teacher and, figuring that Del was guilty anyway, the boy lied on the stand. He simply got caught up in all the excitement of a murder trial. Know what's really odd about this? The same year Randall died, the shadow disappeared on the side of the schoolhouse wall and it never returned."

"That's astounding!" said Mike.

"Yes, but there's a sad note to this story," said Harvey. "The Turnipseeds never told the Kincaid family about Randall's confession."

"What a terrible injustice. So how did you come to know about it?"

Harvey hemmed and hawed before he replied softly, "Randall Turnipseed was Todd's great-great uncle on his mother's side."

Mike shook his head in amazement. *Now everything is beginning to make sense,* he thought. *If Todd is connected to the schoolhouse bricks through an ancestor, maybe I am too.* Shaking Mr. Fisher's hand, Mike said, "Thanks so very much, sir. I've got to run."

"Where are you going?"

"Into the past, Mr. Fisher, into the past."

Mike raced straight to his great aunt Helen, who was born and raised in Rockton. Although she had never seen the shadow herself, she confirmed the story because her father was there the day of the hanging. At Mike's request, she showed him the family tree she had put together over the years. He studied it but found no indication of anyone related to Randall, Kincaid, or the sheriff.

"I thought I had it solved," he moaned.

Aunt Helen reached over and held his hand. "Michael, I have something to tell you. The family tree is not complete. There is a name missing."

"Whose?"

"Del Kincaid. He was your great-great-great uncle. He so shamed our family by committing murder that he was disowned by everyone. I didn't include his name in the family tree."

Mike's head was reeling. *I'm related to Del Kincaid after all. That's the missing link. Now I know why Todd Fisher and I have been seeing the vision of a hanged man.*

The next day, the teacher asked Todd to bring his brick

to school before class. Then Mike put the two bricks side by side on the desk and told the boy the story of the dead man's shadow.

"Todd, I think I have this figured out. We're both having visions of Del Kincaid, the teacher who was put to death on the testimony of Randall Turnipseed. You're related to Randall; I'm related to Del. He was wrongly convicted, and that's why he haunted the schoolhouse with his shadow. Somehow his ghostly energy was revived when you and I—descendants of those involved in the trial—touched these bricks from the schoolhouse."

"So what do we do now?" asked Todd.

"Let's take our bricks and follow me."

They climbed to the top floor of the school and then onto the roof. When it was clear below, they dropped their bricks and watched them smash onto the concrete below.

"I'm pretty sure your headaches and those terrible visions won't be back," the teacher said. "Just don't touch any more bricks from the old schoolhouse, okay?"

"Okay, Mr. Kerr."

"He was innocent, you know."

That night, Mike paid another visit to Aunt Helen. He took out her family tree and grabbed a pen. "It's time we made this family tree more accurate," Mike declared. Then he wrote in the name of Del Kincaid.

Neither Mike nor Todd had those terrible headaches or visions again.

The Mysterious Tapper

"Don't spill any of the water," Remy Burlingame whispered to his roommate, Sean Leicester, as they sneaked down the darkened third-floor hall of Hedley Academy's dormitory.

"I'll be careful," Sean promised.

When they reached the door to the room of fellow students Timothy Barclay and George Figg, Sean set down a bucket of water. He dipped a sponge in the bucket and made a watery trail to the next-door room of Barry Jacoby and Lee Savoy.

Remy and Sean then carefully leaned the bucket of water at an angle against Timothy and George's door.

"Ready?" whispered Remy.

Sean nodded and knocked on the door. The two boys then sprinted lightly down the hall to their own room. They had left their door slightly ajar and kept the room light off so they wouldn't be detected.

Sleepily, Timothy Barclay opened his door, which swung inside, causing the bucket of water to spill into the room. "What the . . . who did this?" Seeing the trail of water lead to his next-door neighbors, Timothy marched over and pounded on their door. "We'll get even with you!"

"Huh?" Barry mumbled. "What are you talking about? It's one in the morning. Go back to sleep."

"Don't rest easy," hissed Timothy. "You'll get yours!"

Meanwhile, in their room down the hall, Remy and Sean buried their heads in their pillows to smother their laughter.

"Nicely done," said Remy.

"Now we've got Timothy and George at war with Barry and Lee."

"Aren't we the *best* practical jokers in school?" Sean said smugly. He pulled out his notebook and marked off two more names on his list of victims. "We've got everybody at least once this term, except for our prize target—Winston Campbell."

Sean, a 14-year-old from Manchester, England, had been at Hedley Academy in London since he was 11. A good student and athlete, Sean loved practical jokes. His main targets were snobby kids who thought they were superior to others. But everyone was fair game. He was so cool that few students realized he was the culprit. He never admitted his role in the jokes and kept a straight face when confronted by victims. He once pretended to be a target himself to avoid being a suspect. He had walked down the hall with whipped cream on his head, complaining someone had sabotaged his cricket cap.

Sean's roommate and partner-in-crime was Remy, a boy who hated being called by his full name of Remington Bedford Burlingame III. Remy shared Sean's delight at having fun at others' expense. He owned a huge collection of fake insects, eyeballs, and human organs, which he enjoyed planting in victims' food, beds, and closets.

Remy didn't act like the stuck-up rich kid he could have become. Give him a T-shirt and torn jeans to wear rather than the school-required blazer and khaki pants, and he would be happy. It didn't matter that his parents were millionaires. The 13-year-old, who had recently enrolled at Hedley, was just one of the guys.

In their darkened room, the roomies were still laughing over the prank when Sean said, "Hey, do you hear dripping water?"

"Yeah, it sounds like it's in our room." Remy turned on the light. "Oh, no!" A water pipe that extended across the ceiling was leaking—as bad luck would have it—directly onto their desks. "My homework!" he moaned. "It's soaked!"

Sean scrambled over to his desk. "My notes from world history class. They're ruined!"

Knowing they couldn't get any maintenance help at this time of night, they tied towels around the leaky joints and set wastebaskets on their desks to catch the drips. Then they turned off the light and went to bed.

TAP . . . THUD . . . TAP . . . THUD . . . TAP . . . THUD.

"Shhh, do you hear that?" asked Sean. He opened the door and looked up and down the hallway. He saw no one. Yet the tapping sound continued.

"What is it?" asked Remy.

Sean closed the door. "Oh, my gosh," he said worriedly. "It's Gerald Rathburn limping on his cane!"

"Gerald Rathburn? The old headmaster? But he's been dead for years."

"It's his ghost!"

"Come on. You don't really believe that old story," said Remy.

TAP . . . THUD . . . TAP . . . THUD . . . TAP . . . THUD.

"When he gets really ticked off, he haunts the hallways of this school. He must be mad at us over our pranks," said Sean.

"Tell me you're making this up," said Remy, beginning to sound scared.

"I wish I was." Sean's eyes got big, and he hopped into bed, throwing the sheets over his head.

Remy turned on the light. He was looking warily around for the ghost when he heard muffled noises coming from under Sean's sheet.

"Sean, are you crying?"

Sean popped his head up and burst out laughing. "I really had you going, didn't I?"

Embarrassed that he had fallen for Sean's joke, Remy fired a pillow at his roomie. "There's no such ghost."

"Of course there isn't," said Sean. "It's just an old legend."

"So what was that noise?"

Sean's smile left. "I don't know. Maybe," he added with a mock look of horror, "it really *was* the ghost of Gerald Rathburn!"

* * *

Gerald Rathburn was a brilliant but eccentric scientist who founded the boys' boarding school in 1873 and named it after his father, Hedley, a noted British philosopher. Gerald believed that students needed to learn the basics, but he also encouraged them to engage in unique and offbeat studies that intrigued them. Among the subjects—which have since been rejected by scientists as nonsense—were phrenology (the study of a person's character by analyzing the shape of the head), numerology (the study of how one's personal numbers such as birth dates can predict the future), and alchemy (the study of changing elements into gold through chemistry).

Rathburn also was fascinated by mummies. He wanted to preserve corpses of famous people and turn them into permanent memorials for display in sealed glass cases. Not surprisingly, most people thought his idea was crazy—and many were convinced he was too.

Nevertheless, Rathburn continued to study mummies of ancient Egyptians, the Mayas of Central America, and the Incas of South America. By the turn of the century he had become an expert and wanted his own corpse preserved for generations to admire. He even wrote in his will exactly how he wanted his wish carried out.

Shortly after he died in 1912, Rathburn's body was preserved according to his directions and placed in a sealed box with a glass front. The display case was then put in the back lobby of the school, where it had remained ever since for visitors to see.

Rathburn physically resembled Benjamin Franklin and

struck a commanding pose seated in one of his favorite chairs. His expression was neither mean nor friendly; more of a no-nonsense yet kindly look. He was dressed in tan breeches, a black coat, white ruffled shirt, white gloves, white stockings, and black shoes. Across his knees rested "Tapper," the name he gave his walking stick. He needed it in the last third of his life because of an arthritic knee that caused him to limp.

"I know it's only a legend, but has anyone ever claimed to have seen Rathburn's ghost?" Remy asked Sean.

"Apparently years ago students who got in trouble saw him," Sean replied. "As a prank they had dismantled the headmaster's car and then reassembled it in the hallway of the administration building. Supposedly Rathburn's ghost was so angry that he made an appearance and scolded the students."

TAP . . . THUD . . . TAP . . . THUD . . . TAP . . . THUD.

"There's that tapping noise again," said Remy. The boys stepped into the hallway. "It's definitely in the hallway."

"And it's getting louder, like it's coming toward us."

"What is it, Sean?"

"I really don't know."

"I feel a chill."

"Yeah, me too. A cold draft. Let's go back inside."

They didn't give the tapping noise much thought the next night. They were too intent on completing their final practical joke of the term.

"I've been waiting for months to do this," said Sean as they tiptoed to Winston Campbell's door shortly after midnight. "Everyone at school knows that Winston is a class-A jerk. He thinks he's so perfect. And the way he tries to get in good with the headmaster makes me sick. He even has a room to himself."

"Yes, it stinks!"

They both laughed because that was exactly what they were going to make happen in Winston's room. Carrying a straightened coat hanger and a capsule of sulfur—a chemical element that smells like rotten eggs—the boys reached Winston's door. Sean spit out the bubblegum he was chewing and stuck it on the end of the coat hanger before lightly attaching it to the capsule. Next, he eased the capsule under Winston's door. With a flick of the wrist, Sean left the capsule under a rug in the center of the room and pulled out the hanger.

"There," he whispered to Remy. "When Winston wakes up and steps on the capsule, he'll break it, and his whole room will stink to high heaven!"

Remy then bent the end of the hanger to form a hook. He shoved it under the door until he hooked the leg of a table. Remy began moving the table in a jerking fashion so the books on top of the table fell off.

Soon the boys heard Winston mutter, "Huh? What's going on?" He turned on a light and stumbled over to the table. "How did this happen? Oh, pee-uuu! Oh, *gross!*"

The boys, trying their best to keep from laughing out loud, quietly dashed back to their room. As they fled the scene, they heard Winston coughing, "Oh, what stinks? This is sickening!"

Once inside their room, the jokesters slapped each

other's hands in celebration for a mission accomplished. Sean got out his notebook to check off the name of the latest victim. He flipped through the pages. "Oh no," he groaned. He turned them back and forth. Then he pounded his fist on the cover and winced.

"Sean, what's wrong?"

"My hit list is missing! I can't find it!"

"How did that happen?"

"This morning on my way to English class, my notebook fell out of my hand. Actually, it felt like someone had yanked it away from me, but no one was around. Papers scattered in all directions. I was positive I had picked them all up. Obviously I didn't." He put his hands to his head and moaned. "If someone finds the hit list, we're marked for revenge!"

Suddenly, the roomies started gagging.

"Yuck!" choked Sean, holding his nose. "The stench in here is terrible!"

"Quick, open the window before I barf!"

"What did you do, Remy?"

"It wasn't me! I thought it was you!"

"Help me with this window. It's stuck." Grunting and groaning, the two boys tried to open it but failed, so they rushed to the door. At first it wouldn't budge, but finally they managed to open it. They staggered into the hallway and took several deep breaths.

"Did someone stink bomb us?" Remy asked.

"Could very well be."

Once the stench left their room, the boys searched everywhere but found no clues to the cause of the smell.

Sitting on his bed, Sean scratched his head and said, "Somebody knows. Somebody is getting even with us."

"Who?"

TAP . . . THUD . . . TAP . . . THUD . . . TAP . . . THUD.

"There's that noise again," said Sean. "Let's try to find out who or what it is."

They followed the strange tapping as it moved to the end of the hallway. It led them down the stairs and out the front door of the dormitory. As they stepped outside, the boys hesitated. It was against the rules to leave the dormitory this late.

"We've got to follow it," Sean declared.

"This is so weird," Remy whispered with a shudder. "It's . . . unearthly."

TAP . . . THUD . . . TAP . . . THUD . . . TAP . . . THUD.

The tapping continued on the sidewalk all the way to the back entrance of the administration building, where the door was slightly ajar. The boys cautiously stepped inside the lobby. Groping in the darkness, they blindly followed the tapping for another few seconds. But then the noise stopped. The boys stood still, waiting for the tapping to continue. Suddenly the lobby lights went on. Remy let out a yelp.

They were standing right in front of the glass case containing Gerald Rathburn.

"Shhh!" Sean ordered. "Do you want to get us in trouble?"

"Sorry, I just got spooked by the old man. Say, did he always have a scowl?"

"I don't think so," replied Sean. He stepped closer and studied the face of the long-dead headmaster, whose lips clearly formed a nasty frown. "That's really odd. I don't remember him looking so angry."

"Come on, Sean, let's get out of here. He gives me the creeps."

"You know what else is strange? That tapping noise led us to Rathburn. I wonder why."

Remy gave a shiver. "You don't think —"

"Look!" said Sean, pointing at Rathburn's lap.

"What? I don't see anything."

"Exactly. His cane—what did he call it? Oh yeah, Tapper—is *gone!*"

Remy gulped. "Do you suppose what we heard was Tapper?"

Before Sean could answer, the burglar alarm went off, and the outside floodlights came on. The panic-stricken boys bolted out the door and raced across the yard back to their dorm and up the steps to their floor.

When they got to their door they couldn't get in. "It's locked!" cried Remy, as he frantically searched his pockets. "Where's the key?"

"I don't have it. I thought you did."

Just then Winston Campbell stepped from his room into the hallway. "Hello, lads. What are you doing up in the wee hours of the morning?"

"We heard a noise out in the hallway," explained Sean. "When we went to investigate, we got locked out."

"Are you sure it wasn't something terribly smelly that got you up?" asked Winston, his eyes glaring suspiciously. As he headed toward the bathroom at the end of the hall, he turned around and asked, "By the way, do you two always sleep with your clothes on?"

"Great," Remy whispered to Sean. "Of all the people to have spotted us, it would be Winston Campbell. Do you think he suspects us?"

Sean glumly nodded. "He probably does, but we've got a bigger problem. Someone might have seen us running from the administration building. And now Winston can say that he saw us in our street clothes in the hallway at the time the burglar alarm went off."

After they plopped down on the floor of the hallway, Remy felt something under him. He scooted over and whispered excitedly, "Look! Our key. It must have fallen out of my pocket somehow."

When they entered their room Sean cautioned, "Don't turn on the lights. If one of the teachers was alerted by the alarm, he might be keeping an eye on the dormitory to see if anyone is up."

The boys hopped into their beds, but Remy couldn't sleep. His mind relived the strange events of the night: the lost list, the stench, the tapping, the opened administration door, the remains of Gerald Rathburn, the scowl, the missing cane, and the room key that mysteriously showed up. And he wondered why the alarm went off as they left the building, but hadn't sounded when they entered it.

Remy rolled over in his bed and suddenly felt an object jab him in the back. He leaped out of bed with a frightened yell.

"What is it, Remy?"

"There's something in my bed! Quick! Turn on the lights!"

Sean flipped on the switch, and the two boys stared in disbelief. Lying on Remy's bed was a walking cane.

"That looks like Gerald Rathburn's cane!" Sean exclaimed. "What's it doing *here*?"

"How should I know? It's in your bed."

"You know I didn't take it."

"Wait a minute," said Sean, nodding his head. "Someone is setting us up. Someone very clever."

"He's going to an awful lot of trouble. What will we do now?"

"Let's sleep on it."

"Yeah, right. Like I'll get any sleep tonight."

The next morning the boys hid the cane above the water pipe in their room and went to breakfast in the mess hall. After finishing their meal, the entire student body waited for morning announcements, which were usually read by a classmate.

But today Headmaster Desmond Guthrie stepped to the microphone. "Gentlemen, I have disturbing news to report," he said. "Apparently, at least two persons tried to break into the administration building shortly after midnight last night. We are taking an inventory to see if anything was taken.

"What is even more upsetting to me is that a member of the faculty saw two persons running from the administration building toward the dormitory. Unfortunately, his view was blocked by the bushes so he couldn't see if anyone actually went into the dorm. If anyone has seen or heard anything, it is your duty to report it to me at once. Dare I say that I sincerely hope that the persons involved in this break-in have no connection to this fine school."

Remy and Sean stared wide-eyed at each other before both looked over to Winston, who glanced at them with a raised eyebrow and a hint of a grin.

Later, as the students filed out of the mess hall, Sean whispered to Remy, "Don't panic. Let's think this out."

Remy bowed his head and gazed at the ground. "They're going to discover that the cane is missing," he moaned. "And then Winston is going to squeal on us, and then they're going to find the cane in our room, and my life as I now know it will be over. And the worst thing about it is that I didn't do anything wrong."

"Maybe they won't notice the cane is gone."

"You saw it was missing right away," said Remy. "We could go to Headmaster Guthrie and tell him the truth."

"Which is . . . ?"

"We heard a strange tapping noise in the hallway, and we followed it outside to the administration building, and . . . oh, right, the story sounds so bad even I'm having trouble believing it."

"Remy, if they conduct a search of the rooms and find the cane, our goose is cooked."

The rest of the day the boys fretted over their fate, wondering when they would be caught and then punished for something they didn't do.

After class the boys hurried back to their room. Sean climbed on his desk and reached for the cane, which he had left on the overhead water pipe. "Remy, it's gone!"

"They must know! Oh, man, we're goners."

"I wonder what they're waiting for. Why doesn't Guthrie put us out of our misery?"

"Sean, I guess we better go and see him."

"Yeah, okay, although I'm still not clear on what we're going to say. The truth is going to sound so bizarre."

Remy reached for the door and turned the handle. "Hey, help me with the door handle. It's stuck."

"Here, let me try." Together they tried to open it. But nothing worked. They pounded on the door, attracting the attention of one of the other boarders.

"What's wrong, lads?" asked Timothy Barclay as he walked by their room.

"We're stuck," Sean replied. "Could you try to push on your side and see if we can get the door open?"

"Hey, fellows," Timothy shouted to others on the floor. "It seems Remy and Sean are stuck in their room and can't get out."

"What a shame," said George Figg.

"Yes, it's a pity." Talking to Remy and Sean through their door, Timothy said, "Well, lads, since you probably won't be joining us for dinner, do you mind if we eat your dessert?"

"Hey, don't leave!" shouted Remy, pounding on the door. "What about us?" Turning to his roommate, he said, "I bet those guys figured out a way to lock us in. They're getting even for all the practical jokes we played on them."

Sean tried to open the window. But it remained stuck—just as it did the previous night. "I don't believe this. We're trapped!"

TAP . . . THUD . . . TAP . . . THUD . . . TAP . . . THUD.

"Sean, the tapping noise!"

"It sounds like it's here in this room!"

"It's awfully cold in here. What's happening?"

"I don't know. It's like an invisible person is in the room with us. If this is a practical joke, it's the best one ever."

"Sean, what if it's not a practical joke? What if it's the ghost of Gerald Rathburn? What if the legend *is* true? The tapping sound could have been his ghost walking with his cane. Maybe he's really mad at us. Don't forget, we saw the scowl on his face. It has to be him!"

Walking around the room like a frightened animal in a cage, Sean declared, "Then I'm never going to pull another practical joke as long as I live! I just want to get out of here!"

Suddenly their door unexplainably creaked open. The boys paused briefly in wonder and then bolted out of the room. They raced down the hall, out of the dormitory, and made a beeline for the administration building.

"Headmaster Guthrie," Remy said breathlessly as the two boys barged into his office. In a rapid-fire voice he babbled, "We were the ones in the administration building last night. We heard a strange tapping sound in the dorm and followed it here and the door was open and we went inside and we saw Gerald Rathburn's face had a scowl and his cane was missing only we didn't take it and then the alarm went off and we ran out of the building and we're innocent . . ."

"Slow down, lad, slow down," ordered Guthrie as he leaned against his desk. "What are you jabbering about?"

Remy and Sean tried to calm down while explaining everything that had happened to them over the last few days.

When they finished, Guthrie wrinkled his nose, folded

his arms, and grinned. "Boys, you are victims of your own imaginations. There are simple explanations for almost all of this. First, we've been having problems with our water lines. Air was getting into them and making a knocking sound that you mistook for tapping.

"Second, I learned what happened last night. There was no break-in. Our maintenance man Henry had disengaged the alarm system because of an electrical short in the basement. He had left the door to the back entrance open while he went to fetch a tool. He turned on the power right after you walked in, so the lights went back on. Unfortunately, he forgot about the alarm system and set it off. As for Tapper and Rathburn's scowl, let's go see."

They walked across the hall and examined the glass case containing the old headmaster. The boys were stunned by what they saw. Tapper was sitting across Rathburn's lap as it had for decades.

"Obviously, the cane is there," said Guthrie. "Now, Remy, look at his face. You're not going to tell me that's a scowl, are you?"

"No, sir. It's his usual expression. I must have been mistaken."

"I can't explain why you got trapped in your room or smelled a bad odor, although I have a pretty good idea," Guthrie said. "We know that you two have been pulling pranks on your fellow students. Sean, someone found your hit list. I suspect that your classmates were paying you back."

"I guess you're right, sir," Sean said sheepishly. "We've learned our lesson."

"Good," said the headmaster. "But apparently there is one lesson you haven't learned—obeying curfew. Since you violated it, you two are confined to your quarters for the weekend. That is all."

After leaving the office, Remy turned to Sean and said, "You and I both know the tapping wasn't caused by water pipe problems. Not everything that happened was from the boys pulling practical jokes on us."

"Grow up, Remy. Of course it was them. And I wouldn't be surprised if Guthrie was in on the cane joke. You had me believing Gerald Rathburn's ghost was to blame. There is no ghost. It's just a legend."

Remy smiled weakly. "I suppose you're right."

As they walked past Gerald Rathburn's display case, Remy grabbed Sean's arm and spun him around.

"What is it, Remy?"

Remy, wide-eyed and speechless, pointed to Gerald Rathburn's face. The shocked boys could plainly tell that the no-nonsense yet kindly expression of the old headmaster had changed. This time, the dead man's thin lips had formed a sly smile.